Th...
WEB SITE
Guide 2001

The Cool
WEB SITE
Guide 2001

GRAHAM EDMONDS

ORION

First published in 2001 by Orion Media
An imprint of Orion Books Ltd
Orion House, 5 Upper St Martin's Lane,
London WC2H 9EA

A CIP catalogue record for this book is
available from the British Library.

ISBN 0 75284 169 6

Designed by Staziker Jones, Cardiff

Printed by Clays Ltd, St Ives plc

Contents

7 Acknowledgements

9 Introduction

13 Advice

22 Aircraft

23 Astrology and horoscopes

24 Cars and motorbikes

27 Cartoons

29 Celebrities

30 Chat

34 Finding something

37 Food

39 Games

59 Greetings cards

60 Homework

97 Movies

102 Music and radio

122 News and weather

124 On-line magazines

133 Pets

137 Phones and phone numbers

142 Sci-Fi and fantasy

147 Shopping

171 Sport

188 Student

192 Travel

194 TV

204 Web cameras

205 Stop press

208 Index

Acknowledgements

Firstly mega-thanks to Claire Nuttall for all her help and advice and for being the voice of teenagers everywhere. Without her help this could have been a very boring book.

Secondly to Deborah Gray for keeping my writing in line, giving me a mum's eye view and particularly for the section for students.

Lastly to Michaela for love and huge support.

Introduction

This book is designed to help you get the most out of the internet and to show how exciting the world wide web can be.

The internet can be used for a huge number of things, for instance looking up your favourite band (**www.clickmusic.co.uk**), finding out what they're up to, when the next single is released or whether there are other bands that are similar in style. You can also find out how you can download music for free.

What about TV or the movies, what's on and when? Try **www.popcorn.co.uk**. What about an on-line magazine that really covers your interests in a way that a normal magazine can't? There are hundreds but we've picked the best, the most wicked and the most entertaining.

Using the internet for game playing is one of the best things about it. There's a section on all the different types of games, where to buy and download updates, as well as play.

Talking of spending money, another great use of the internet is buying stuff much cheaper than in a normal shop and getting it delivered to your home. OK, so your parents may not let you have use of a credit card but there are ways round that. Try visiting **www.y-creds.co.uk**.

If you like sports then there are hundreds of

sites you can use to keep up to date, or maybe you'd like to travel – you can, virtually.

Then there's homework. We've chosen a whole wodge of sites that will help, from those that cover the entire curriculum such as **www.homeworkelephant.co.uk** to specialists that help with one topic. If you want to look something up, there's a site that will help. If it's not listed, then we'll show you how to search it out.

There are loads of ways to keep in contact with your friends and even make new ones. We'll show you how in our Chat section.

One of the best sections of the book is that on Advice, where you can get help on all sorts of topics from bullying, illness or careers. It sums up all that's best about the world wide web: a community of people try to help others to help themselves and doing it in an enjoyable way.

PICK OF THE SITES

Here is *The Cool Web Site Guide's* top ten sites. These have that WOW factor that make them something special.

1 **www.bbc.co.uk**
2 **www.embarrassingproblems.co.uk**

3 **www.dv.com**
4 **www.popworld.co.uk**
5 **www.beritsbest.com**
6 **www.y-creds.co.uk**
7 **www.reachforthesky.co.uk**
8 **www.wowgo.com**
9 **www.shockwave.com**
10 **www.popcorn.co.uk**

USING THE BOOK

The book is arranged by category in alphabetical order, we've also provided a short index to help find your way around.

Each site we visit is reviewed, and we look at things like:

- how much information there is
- how up to date it is
- how fast it downloads
- how easy it is to find your way around
- how good it is to look at
- if it sells stuff, is it good value?

These all come together to give the site its 'cool rating', the more ☺'s it gets, the better the site. **So here's the book, use it wisely and enjoy.**

Adults are genuinely concerned about dishonest and corrupt people taking advantage of children and teenagers using the internet. In truth it's quite easy to 'meet' unsuitable people, access pornography or get violent games; this book isn't about telling you how to do that, but neither is it full of dire warnings or nods and winks to parents.

You just need to be wary and treat the internet as you would any strange place, be aware and act with caution. The internet can be a fascinating and rewarding place to visit, but remember if something looks dodgy or you don't feel comfortable, do what you'd normally do – go somewhere else.

Advice and helplines

The internet is a great place for tracking down information, and is especially useful when it comes to those things you'd rather discover independently with no involvement from parents or even friends. Here are some great sites where you can get impartial advice on subjects such as careers, finance, health and yes, sex as well.

General advice sites

www.childline.co.uk
SUPPORT WHEN YOU NEED IT

☺☺☺☺☺
COUNTRY UK

Childline's web site is chock full of information on many problems that face us, including fact sheets on topics such as coping with death, AIDS, even safe surfing on the net. Grapevine, their on-line mag has loads of advice as well as celebrity features and web site listings.

www.samaritans.co.uk
THE SAMARITANS

☺☺☺☺
COUNTRY UK

This site shows how to contact them, what they do and where to go for the best advice.

www.thesite.org.uk
THE SITE
☺☺☺☺

COUNTRY UK

These guys offer advice on a range of subjects; careers, relationships, drugs, sex, money, legal issues and so on. Aimed largely at 15 to 24 year olds.

www.teenadviceonline.com
TALK TO SOMEONE
☺☺☺

COUNTRY USA

OK, not the coolest site, but there are some good articles and you can e-mail a volunteer counsellor of your choosing to get personal advice and help. They reply quickly and they are straight-up and sympathetic. You can share experiences of those who have already gone through trauma in the archives section.

www.childrens-express.org
IN THE NEWS
☺☺☺

COUNTRY UK

An on-line newspaper that covers issues that affect children. Written largely by children, the archives contain useful information on a large number of topics and issues. It's up-to-date and a good read, if nothing else.

www.teencentral.net
ADVICE THROUGH STORIES
☺☺

COUNTRY USA

Here you can read through the thoughts, concerns, anxieties and experiences of others, anonymously and safely. However, the registration process is a pain, and because of it, from the UK you can only get access to a small amount of what looks like lots of good stuff.

www.youngminds.org.uk
MENTAL HEALTH MATTERS

☺☺☺

COUNTRY UK

A serious site principally for adults but with thorough on-line booklets for young people on issues such as child abuse, self harm, school-related problems and depression. The links for young people are helpful too.

SPECIFIC ISSUES *(alphabetically by subject)*

Bullying

www.bullying.co.uk
HOW TO COPE WITH BULLYING

☺☺☺☺

COUNTRY UK

Advice for everyone on how to deal with a bully; there are sections with tips for dealing with them, school projects, problem pages and links to related sites.

Careers

www.careerguide.net
INTERNET CAREER DIRECTORY

☺☺☺☺

COUNTRY UK

A huge web site dedicated to careers and job seeking, the Career Advice section has information on how to write a C.V., interview techniques and links to related and useful web sites.

www.careers-gateway.co.uk
THE CAREER GATEWAY

☺☺☺☺

COUNTRY UK

Great advice and lots of information, for example what you should do with your exam results, what options are open to you and articles that help you decide what you can do with your life.

www.reachforthesky.co.uk
CAREER ADVICE FROM SKY TV

☺☺☺☺☺

COUNTRY UK

Sky has put together a groovy web site that lives up to its design. There are interviews, examples and information on careers, as well as a section where you can just chill out and win lots of fab things. The questionnaire is a bit of fun and may give you a pointer to your personality and what type of career might suit you.

www.dfee.gov.uk
DON'T KNOW WHAT TO DO NEXT?

☺☺☺☺

COUNTRY UK

If you're undecided about which subjects to take at 14 go to Which Way Now, which helps you to decide whether to take GCSE physical education or physics. If you're 16 and need to choose between staying at school or moving on, It's Your Choice may help. Young people with disabilities should try www.after16.org.uk. For links go to www.connexions.gov.uk.

Drugs

www.nodrugs.org.uk
YOU DON'T NEED DRUGS TO FEEL GOOD

☺☺☺ Information on the effects of taking drugs, what
COUNTRY UK they do and how to get help. There are facts and figures on everything from alcohol to ecstasy to tobacco as well as some good advice.

www.urban75.com/Drugs
DRUGS – A STRAIGHTFORWARD GUIDE

☺☺☺☺ Urban 75 is a streetwise e-zine, which is fun
COUNTRY UK and free of annoying adverts. It has an excellent overview on drugs, what they do and how they affect you. There's no preaching or recommendations, just good information.

Finance

www.young-money.co.uk
ON-LINE MONEY GAME SHOW

☺☺☺ Are you a financial whiz kid of the future?
COUNTRY UK Here's a relatively fun and painless way of

learning about the world of finance. You need Shockwave for it to work.

www.blays.co.uk
BLAYS GUIDES
☺☺☺☺   Excellent design and impartial advice make the
COUNTRY UK   Blays Guide a great place to visit for personal finance. It has all the usual suspects: banking, savings etc. Also a good section for students.

Health

www.embarrassingproblems.com
STRAIGHT TALK, GOOD ADVICE
☺☺☺☺☺   Written by a well-respected doctor, this brilliant
COUNTRY UK   site covers all those rather personal health issues that you'd prefer to investigate yourself in the first instance. It's quick and easy to use with lots of links to related sites. If you can't find what you need here try **www.prematuree.com**, which is especially useful for older teenage girls.

www.iemily.com
GIRLS' HEALTH
☺☺☺☺   A massive A–Z listing of issues and problems
COUNTRY USA   you might encounter. It's easy-to-use and the information is straight to the point and often accompanied by articles relating to the subject.

www.fiteen.com
YOUR FITNESS STARTS HERE
☺☺☺☺ Sensible eating, how to exercise properly and the
COUNTRY USA latest health news.

Racism

www.britkid.org
DEALING WITH RACISM
☺☺☺☺ Racial issues transformed into a game exploring
COUNTRY UK how different ethnic groups live in the Britain of
today.

It's full of interesting facts and information.
The site's serious side deals with racism and
provides background information on the various
races and their religious beliefs.

www.blackbritain.co.uk
FOR BLACK BRITAIN
☺☺☺☺ This is a lifestyle site with information on a huge
COUNTRY UK number of topics from clubbing to shopping to
the latest news. It also offers a great deal of info
on jobs and careers, as well as help with legal
issues and spiritual advice.

Relationships, love and sex

www.breakupgirl.com
SAVING LOVE – LIVES THE WORLD OVER

☺ ☺ ☺

COUNTRY USA

Break Up Girl gives advice on what to do when lurve goes blind, how to cope with rejection and how to get that replacement! Serious and fun at the same time, and lots of gossip too.

www.adolescentadulthood.com
FLIRTING, DATING AND DUMPING

☺ ☺ ☺

COUNTRY USA

A sort of guide to getting, keeping and getting rid of lovers, with advice on kissing and even a jokes page. There's also a specific section for guys with advice on romance and how to impress on the first date, amongst other things.

www.lovelife.uk.com
HERE TO ANSWER YOUR QUESTIONS

☺ ☺ ☺ ☺

COUNTRY UK

Great site that has lots of stuff on sex as well as games and links to related sites. The emphasis is on safe sex and AIDS prevention. See also the Terence Higgins Trust at www.tht.org.uk; this is the leading AIDS charity.

www.fpa.org.uk
FAMILY PLANNING ASSOCIATION

☺ ☺ ☺ ☺

COUNTRY UK

Straightforward and informative, you can find out where to get help and there's a good list of web links too.

www.positive.org
COALITION FOR POSITIVE SEXUALITY

☺☺☺

COUNTRY USA

Born out of Chicago High Schools, this is put together by students and offers good advice on sex. The aim is to give you the information that you need to take care of yourself, safely. It's upfront and very American in style. See also the very boring **www.allaboutsex.org**, which has also has loads of info.

Stress

www.at-ease.nsf.org.uk
YOUR MENTAL HEALTH

☺☺☺☺

COUNTRY UK

At-ease offers loads of good advice on how to deal with stress and is aimed specifically at young people. Go to the A-Z section which covers a large list of subjects from dealing with aggression to exam stress to how to become a volunteer to help others.

www.isma.org.uk/exams.htm
EXAM STRESS

☺☺☺

COUNTRY UK

Top tips on coping with exams from the International Stress Management Association.

Aircraft

www.flyer.co.uk
AVIATION IN THE UK

☺ ☺ ☺ ☺

COUNTRY UK

News, views and information on aviation from the Flyer Magazine site. You'll find a good section on aviation links, details on how to buy and sell an aircraft, classified ads and there's even free internet access. Check out www.pilotweb.co.uk as well.

www.aeroflight.co.uk
AVIATION ENTHUSIASTS

☺ ☺ ☺ ☺

COUNTRY UK

A good site that attempts to be an 'information stop' for all aviation enthusiasts. It has details on the world's air forces, a section on the media including specialist books and bookshops as well as details of air shows and museums.

Astrology and horoscopes

www.astrology.com
ASTROLOGICAL GUIDANCE
☺☺☺   A really big site offering free advice from the
COUNTRY UK   stars. You can buy a personalised reading and
chart or just browse the more general horoscopes. You can find celebrity horoscopes too
and learn about the history and techniques of
astrology.

www.excite.co.uk/horoscopes/
FREE DAILY HOROSCOPES
☺☺☺   Excite is a fun search engine with a section
COUNTRY UK   devoted to horoscopes. You can get daily read-
ings or rate your romance, and if you get bored
with that, then check out the love-o-meter or
snap a virtual fortune cookie.

www.horoscopes4u.com
A HOROSCOPE DIRECTORY
☺☺☺☺   Whether it's daily, monthly or yearly you'll find
COUNTRY USA   it here, plus masses of links to other sites. There
are also sections on romance, finance and astro-
logical chat.

Cars and motorbikes

See also **Motorsport,** *page181*

www.dvla.gov.uk
DRIVER AND VEHICLE LICENSING AGENCY
☺☺☺☺☺ If you need the official line in motoring, the
COUNTRY UK   driver's section has details on getting a licence,
licence changes and medical issues. The vehicles
section goes through all related forms and there's
also a what's new page. It's clearly and concisely
written throughout, and information is easy to
find.

www.autoexpress.co.uk
THE BEST MOTORING NEWS AND INFORMATION
☺☺☺☺ Massive database on cars, with motoring news
COUNTRY UK   and features on the latest models, you can check
prices too. It also has classified ads and a great
set of links. You have to register to get access to
most of the information.

www.topgear.beeb.com
TOP GEAR MAGAZINE
☺☺☺☺ Whether you want to check out the on-line show
COUNTRY UK   room, learn about the car business or get the
weekly e-mail from the lovely Vicki, the *Top
Gear* magazine is a great car mag.

www.classicmotor.co.uk
FOR CLASSIC CARS

☻ ☻ ☻

COUNTRY UK

Probably the best classic car site, it's got loads of info including clubs, classifieds and books; here you can buy anything from a car to a light bulb. It's not the easiest site to navigate though – it's a bit of a mess actually.

www.pistonheads.com
BEST OF BRITISH MOTORING

☻ ☻ ☻ ☻

COUNTRY UK

Pistonheads is a cool British site dedicated to the faster side of motoring and is great for reviews of the latest cars. They're passionate about their subject and very informative too.

www.driving.co.uk
PASS YOUR TEST

☻ ☻ ☻ ☻

COUNTRY UK

For some more good advice try BSM's site, it has mock tests and lots of information to help you pass whatever the type of test you take. Check out the informative **www.learners.co.uk**, which has good links to related sites. Also keep an eye out for **www.cyberdrive.co.uk**, which was being revamped at time of writing. It used to provide a good on-line driving test so hopefully they are just trying to improve things.

Also check out the AA at **www.theaa.co.uk** or the RAC at **www.rac.co.uk**, especially good for traffic information.

www.motorcycle.uk.com
MOTORBIKES

☺☺☺☺   If it's not on the site there will be a link to it.
COUNTRY UK   This is a really informative site with lots of features on subjects from parts, to clubs and even technical help. It just looks a bit boring. For a bit more excitement but less info try **www.bikenet.com** which is more of a magazine and has reviews and a chat section.

Cartoons

www.aardman.com
HOME OF WALLACE, GROMMIT AND ANGRY KID

☺☺☺☺☺ This brilliant site takes a while to download but

COUNTRY UK it's worth the wait, there's news on what the team are up to, links to their films, a shop and an inside story on how it all began. It's worth it for the link to the Angry Kid pages at Atom Films alone – go to **www.atomfilms.com** if you want to check them out.

www.cartoonnetwork.co.uk
CARTOON NETWORK

☺☺☺☺ OK so it's not exactly for teenagers, but you

COUNTRY UK watch it don't you? This site has lots of games, news and schedule information as well as feature pages on the main cartoons – Scooby, Ed, Edd 'n' Eddy, Tom and Jerry and Dragonball Z to name but a few.

www.disney.co.uk
DISNEY UK

☺☺☺☺ The British Disney site is less commercial than the

COUNTRY UK American (**www.disney.com**) one so more enjoyable to visit. It has all the usual favourites plus a selection of games and features. There's also an interactive archive of all the Disney characters.

www.thesimpsons.com
THE OFFICIAL SIMPSONS SITE

☺☺☺☺

COUNTRY USA

If you can't get enough of the Simpsons on TV then try this for size, there's chat, biographies and an episode guide in case you need to look anything up.

It's a little slow so you may want to try the British fan site dedicated them at www.buzzcola.co.uk/simpsons/home.html, where you can buy merchandise on top of all the usual things like links and the episode guide.

www.southparkuk.freeserve.co.uk/
SOUTH PARK UK

☺☺☺

COUNTRY UK

A really good site for SP fans with lots of information, news and downloads of games and episodes. For another good UK site try www.blakeburn.freeuk.com/.

Celebrities

Find your favourite celebrities and their web sites using these on-line directories.

www.celebritysearchengine.co.uk
THE CELEBRITY SEARCH ENGINE

☺☺☺☺   Type in the name of the celebrity that you're
COUNTRY UK   looking for and a list of sites appears. All sites
                are rated 1–10, a short description is given plus
                the link to the chosen site.

www.celebrityemail.com
E-MAIL THE STARS

☺☺☺☺   E-mail addresses for over 18,000 of the world's
COUNTRY USA   most famous people. It's quite biased towards
                Americans but give it a try anyway, you might
                get a reply.

Chat

There are literally thousands of chat sites and rooms on the web, covering loads of different topics. A chat program is a great way to keep in contact with friends, especially if they live miles away.

This is the area of the net that parents have most concerns about, and there have been loads of cases where teenagers have been tricked into giving personal information and even into meetings. Here are our top tips for keeping the weirdos at bay.

Chat – *Cool Web Site Guide*'s Top Tips

1. Be wary, just like you would be if you were visiting any new place.
2. Don't give your e-mail address out without making sure that only the person you're sending it to can read it.
3. People often pretend to be someone they're not when they're chatting. Unless you know the person, assume that's the case with anyone you chat with.
4. Don't meet up with anyone you've met online; keep your on-line life separate. Chances are they'd be a let-down, even if they were genuine.

5. If you like the look of a chat room or site, but you're not sure about it, ask an adult to check it out for you first.
6. If you want to meet up with friends on-line, arrange a time and place beforehand.
7. If you don't like someone, block 'em.
8. Check out the excellent **www.chatdanger.com** for more info on how to chat safely.

These are the major chat sites and programs:

www.aol.com
AOL INSTANT MESSENGER
☺ ☺ ☺ ☺ ☺ One of the most popular, it's pretty safe and,
COUNTRY UK anyway, you can easily block people who are a nuisance or just set it up so that only friends can talk to you. You can also decide how much information about you other users can see.

www.delphi.com
DELPHI FORUMS
☺ ☺ ☺ ☺ A forum is a place where people chat, a bit like
COUNTRY USA sitting round a table. Delphi has loads of forums and it's easy to get involved. You can even start your own forum if you like. It has to be said that some are a bit weird though, so be careful.

www.freezone.com

WHERE KIDS CONNECT

☺☺☺☺

COUNTRY USA

Lots more than just chat, there's games, quizzes, links and you can construct your own home page. You don't need to download a special program here, but you do have to register to join in although they guarantee not to use your personal info.

www.kidsnation.com

CHAT LIVE AT THE COOLEST KID'S PALACE

☺☺☺☺

COUNTRY USA

Monitored by adults so you'll not get any unwanted intrusions, you just download the Palace software and off you go. Not as good-looking as some sites but it works well.

www.mirabilis.com

ICQ – I SEEK YOU

☺☺☺☺

COUNTRY UK

Not so easy for the very young but there's lots here and it's quick. There's lots of features such as games, money advice, music and lurve. As a bonus it's easy-to-use combined with a mobile phone.

www.mirc.com

IRC – INTERNET RELAY CHAT

☺☺☺

COUNTRY USA

A straightforward chat program, easy-to-use, now overtaken by the likes of MSN and AOL but some web sites may still use it.

www.hayseed.net/MOO/

MOO AND MUD

ت ت ت ت A MOO is a program that enables you to go to a
COUNTRY USA place on a computer where you can talk to
others; a MUD is a sort of MOO. Schools are
getting into MOOs in a big way. Find out all you
need to know at this site – it's easy once you get
your head around it – honest.

www.msn.com

MICROSOFT MSN MESSENGER

ت ت ت ت Easy-to-use but it can be confusing as Microsoft
COUNTRY USA is so keen for you to use other parts of their
massive site you'll often find yourself suddenly
transferred. The best bet is to customise it so
that there's no mistake.

Finding something

Can't find what you're looking for? These sites can help you; firstly by searching the internet and the world wide web for key words or by acting as a sort of telephone directory of sites.

This is another area of the internet that parents worry about because it's easy to access something unsuitable or nasty.

Many sites send out something called a 'cookie' to your computer as soon as you access them. These are programs designed to find information out about you and where you go on the net, they may even alter settings on your PC. Some shopping sites can't function without cookies, but you must remember that some dodgy sites use information from cookies in a dodgy way. Best avoid them.

These sites are all considered safe.

Search Engines

www.ajkids.com

ASK JEEVES

☺ ☺ ☺ ☺   In his various guises Jeeves is one of the most

COUNTRY USA   popular search engines in use. All you do is type

in your question and you'll get a selection of
sites to visit.

www.yahooligans.com
YAHOO!

☺☺☺☺☺ Great for searching, easy-to-use and with lots of
COUNTRY USA other added features such as games, news and
homework help.

Directories

www.all4kidsuk.com
THE KID'S DIRECTORY

☺☺☺ Aimed at younger children and their parents,
COUNTRY UK this isn't an obvious choice for teenagers, but
if you're stuck for something to do on a wet
Saturday afternoon you could do worse than
pay them a visit. It's got an easy-to-use search
engine, where you can search by county if
you need to. If you're still stuck try
www.kidsnet.co.uk, which is similar and
covers different areas of the country.

www.beritsbest.com
SITES FOR CHILDREN

☺☺☺☺☺ Over 1000 sites in this directory split into six
COUNTRY USA major categories: fun, things to do, nature, serious stuff (homework), chat and surfing. Each
site is rated for speed and content and you can
suggest new sites as well. Another similar site to

Berits is **www.kids-space.org**, which has some
really cute graphics and a better search facility.

www.teen.com
THE ULTIMATE PLACE FOR TEENS

Annoying adverts aside, this is a great site for
teenagers, it's more of a magazine than anything
ಲಾ ಲಾ ಲಾ ಲಾ   but it's here because of the search engine which

COUNTRY USA   is excellent. It can be a little slow though.

www.teensites.org
WEB DIRECTORY FOR TEENS

A huge directory of sites covering loads of
subjects of interest to teenagers, the only down-
ಲಾ ಲಾ ಲಾ ಲಾ   side is that it's biased to the USA. If you don't

COUNTRY USA   mind that, then it should have everything you
need.

Food

For those of you who like to cook your own food, here are some sites to inspire you.

www.simplyfood.co.uk
ALL ABOUT FOOD

☺☺☺☺☺ One of the best designed web sites for anyone
COUNTRY UK who loves food and, even if you're just starting
to cook for yourself, there are loads of recipes.
Take a look at the quick-and-easy recipe section
which has 10 new meals to try each week. You
can also see what the latest celebrities are up to
and even chat to one sometimes.

www.jamieoliver.net
PUKKA!

☺☺☺☺ Find out what Jamie Oliver is up to in his do-
COUNTRY UK lally diary, get some recipes and sample some of
his music via his other web sites, or join the kid's
club where there are some easy recipes to try.
Nice site Jamie.

www.vegsoc.org
THE VEGETARIAN SOCIETY

☺☺☺☺ This is the official site of the UK branch and
COUNTRY UK is split into ten sections: news, new veggies,

environment, business opportunities, recipes and the cookery school, health, membership info and on-line bookstore. Each section is packed with information, written in plain English and there is a search engine for information on any veggie topic. There's an excellent section for young people with some good links to related web sites.

Games

There's a massive selection of games on the net, from board games to quizzes to your everyday 'shoot 'em up' type experience. Here's just some of the very best.

Adults (parents in particular) will be concerned about the level of violence you encounter in some games. Our advice is to choose wisely if you want to keep playing!

Before downloading a game it's wise to check it for viruses – always. If you've not got virus software on your PC then you can obtain a good one free from Innoculate at http://antivirus.cai.com

Finding games

http://gamespotter.com
GAMES SEARCH ENGINE
☺☺☺☺

COUNTRY USA

A really handy site with links to virtually every type of game whether it be a puzzle or action. Alternatively, you can use the search facility to find something. Each game featured on the list is reviewed.

www.electricgames.com
LINKS AND REVIEWS
☺☺☺☺☺

COUNTRY USA

A good combination of search engine, links and reviews make Electric Games a good starting place on your quest for the perfect game. Where many other sites overload on information, this is well laid out and easy-to-use, especially if you're new to it all.

Games magazines

www.avault.com
THE ADRENALINE VAULT

☺☺☺☺
COUNTRY USA A comprehensive games magazine with demos, reviews and features on software and hardware – it looks good too. There's also an OK cheats and hints section.

www.gamespy.com
GAMINGS HOMEPAGE

☺☺☺☺
COUNTRY USA Lots here, apart from the usual reviews and features. There are chat and help sections plus links to the Arcade with over 150 free games to play.

www.gameplay.com
THE GATEWAY TO GAMES

☺☺☺☺☺
COUNTRY USA A really nice design helps make Gameplay one of the most visited games sites. Its magazine (Spank!) is good and up-to-date and you're taken to the Wireplay site to play games on-line. You can buy games too.

www.gamers.com
A MOMENT ENJOYED IS NOT WASTED

☺ ☺ ☺ ☺ ☺ A great-looking site with all the features you'd

COUNTRY USA expect from a games magazine but it has more in the way of downloads and games to play. There is also a chat section and competitions.

www.gamesdomain.co.uk
THE GAMES DOMAIN

☺ ☺ ☺ ☺ ☺ A strong combination of freebies, competitions,

COUNTRY UK good links, news and reviews make this site a great place to start on-line gaming. It's clear, fast and easy-to-use.

www.gameweek.com
GAMES NEWS

☺ ☺ ☺ A very newsy site with lots on the latest develop-

COUNTRY USA ments and upcoming games, more for the industry than the normal punter but good if you want to keep in the know.

www.happypuppy.com
GAMES REVIEWED

☺ ☺ ☺ ☺ ☺ Happy Puppy has been around a while now

COUNTRY USA reviewing games in all the major formats. Each is given a thorough test, then it's rated and given a written review. There are also links to related games sites. It's all packaged on a really good web site which is quick and user friendly.

www.pcgame.com
ALL ON ONE SITE

☺☺☺☺
COUNTRY UK
The idea is to get as much on one site about games and gaming as possible in a simple package and it largely succeeds. The design is great, the information up to the minute and the links work. There's more than enough information including reviews, cheats and demos of the latest games.

Games to play

www.barrysworld.com
GAMES ON-LINE

☺☺☺☺
COUNTRY UK
Barrysworld specialise in providing on-line servers suitable for playing their own brand games and you can take part in several from this site. There's also more information and links than you'll ever need, which makes it a little daunting at first, but it's also helpful and very well written.

www.classicgaming.com
OLD CLASSIC GAMES REVIVED

☺☺☺☺
COUNTRY USA
Probably one for dad but there's some good stuff on here so it's at least worth a look and it's amazing how new some of the games are.

www.smallrockets.com
NEW WEB SITE FROM A NEW COMPANY

☺☺   This well designed and good looking site doesn't
COUNTRY UK   have many games at the moment but what it
does have are high quality. This is one to watch
for the future.

www.freegames.org
OVER 700 FREE GAMES

☺☺☺☺   Enough to keep you occupied for hours with
COUNTRY USA   games of every type from board to action to
puzzles and sports. There's also a really good set
of links to other sites. It's worth checking out
www.freeloader.com, which has a more modern
selection available but you have to register and
jump through a few hoops to get them.

www.gamearchive.com
PINBALL MACHINES

☺☺☺   A site devoted to pinball machines and similar
COUNTRY USA   games put together by real fans. There's also a
selection of video games and links to similar
sites.

www.gamebrew.com
JAVA GAMING

☺☺☺

COUNTRY USA

The Java program gives gaming an extra edge with brilliant graphics in particular. Gamebrew specialise in Java games and there are some brilliant ones to download and play here. Send them to your friends...

http://games.yahoo.com
YAHOO!

☺☺☺

COUNTRY USA

The world's favourite search engine has its own games section where you can play against others or yourself on-line. The emphasis is on board games, puzzles and quizzes although there are other games available plus links to games sites.

www.ogl.org
ON-LINE GAMING LEAGUE

☺☺☺☺

COUNTRY USA

Join a community of gamers who play in leagues for fun. You can play all the major on-line games and compete in the leagues and ladders if you like. To quote them, 'What matters is that people are meeting and interacting with other people on the internet via our services and their game'.

www.pokemon.co.uk
POKEMON GAMES FANS GO HERE
☺☺☺☺   If you're into Pokemon there are games to play,
COUNTRY UK   download and buy, links, news, latest updates,
             cartoons and comics.

www.planetquake.com
THE EPICENTRE OF QUAKE
☺☺☺☺☺   *Quake* is the most popular game played on the
COUNTRY USA internet, and this slightly slow site gives you all
             the background and details on the game. It's got
             loads of links and features as well as reviews and
             chat.

www.shockwave.com
SHOCKWAVE GRAPHICS
☺☺☺☺☺   Shockwave's fantastic site offers much more
COUNTRY USA than games, namely, cartoons, greeting cards and
             music. Click on Games and you get access to six
             sections; action, adventure, sports, jigsaws and
             board games as well as two sections of arcade
             games. The graphics are superb.

www.surfmonkey.com
GAMES FOR KIDS
☺☺☺☺   Although primarily a colourful kid's site, the
COUNTRY USA games section of Surf Monkey offers over 500
             games from the very simple to the quite compli-
             cated. Great for beginners.

www.lysator.liu.se/tolkien-games/
LORD OF THE RINGS
☺☺☺☺☺ Get immersed in Tolkien's *Middle Earth* with
COUNTRY SWEDEN some 100 games all based on the story. It's got
action games, quizzes and puzzles, strategy
games and of course role-playing games.

www.videogames.org
HOME VIDEO GAME HISTORY
☺☺ An odd site that basically consists of links to
COUNTRY USA other sites that specialise in video games,
although there are some older games on site.
That's it really.

www.wireplay.com
THE GAMES NETWORK
☺☺☺☺☺ Gameplay's free games site is excellent. The site
COUNTRY USA supports a good selection of on-line games on
their server all with good graphics. This is
combined with news, updates, demos and
patches (files that update current games).

www.womengamers.com
BECAUSE WOMEN DO PLAY
☺☺☺☺ The selection of games available and those
COUNTRY USA reviewed are geared to a female audience (although
there's plenty here for men to enjoy too). It has up-
to-the-minute reviews, really well-written articles,
lots of content and high quality design.

www.zone.com
MICROSOFT GAMES ZONE

☺☺☺☺

COUNTRY USA

With over 100 games to choose from, you shouldn't be disappointed. If you don't mind paying the subscription, take a look at their premium selection which are highly inventive multiplayer games. There's also a selection of games to buy.

Game manufacturers and console games

www.dreamcast.com
DREAMCAST FROM SEGA

☺☺☺☺

COUNTRY USA

Get the latest information on what's coming, try them out or play on-line, you can also get the latest technology. See also www.dreamcastmag.co.uk and www.dreamcastmagazine.com for more information, reviews and games.

www.eidosnet.co.uk
EIDOS

☺☺☺☺

COUNTRY UK

Sign up to Eidosnet the server and you get access to games via www.mplayer.com Eidos themselves are responsible for games like *Tomb Raider* and *Championship Manager*. This method gives better than average quality and on-line access but you are tied to their games.

www.gbstation.com
GAME BOY NEWS

☺ ☺ ☺ ☺

COUNTRY USA

Here you can get all the latest information on *Game Boy*, plus reviews and features such as chat forums and cheats. You can also buy from the site.

www.hasbrointeractive.com
HASBRO GAMES

☺ ☺ ☺

COUNTRY USA

No games to download, but there are details of all the games they sell and you can get patches on the site. The most useful bit is the links to sites that either sell or allow you to play on-line.

www.nintendo.com
OFFICIAL NINTENDO

☺ ☺ ☺ ☺

COUNTRY USA

Get the latest news from Nintendo and its spin offs – *N64*, *Game Boy* and *Game Cube*. There's also information on the hardware and details of the games new and old. For further information try the superbly designed **www.n64europe.com**, which is brilliant for news and information. For a site with wider Nintendo info go to **www.nintendojo.com**.

http://uk.playstation.com
OFFICIAL PLAYSTATION SITE

☺ ☺ ☺

COUNTRY USA

Looks good but doesn't tell you much except where to buy plus some background information on the history of *Playstation*. For a more positive experience check out www.psxnews.com, which is good looking and has forums, news, reviews and previews or www.psx2unicom.com or maybe www.psxextreme.com or even www.absolute-playstation.com. They all do the same job, just pick the one you like best.

www.planetxbox.com

INFORMATION ON XBOX

☺ ☺ ☺ ☺ *Xbox* is Microsoft's new toy and this site gives

COUNTRY USA you the latest information on it. It promises much and will be released in the States late 2001.

www.station.sony.com

SONY ON-LINE GAMES

☺ ☺ ☺ ☺ ☺ Sony have put together an exceptional site for

COUNTRY USA on-line gaming, and with over 6 million members it's one of the most popular, being well-designed and easy-to-use. There are lots of games to choose from, even official ones such as *Trivial Pursuit*. Providing you can put up with the adverts, it's a real treat to use.

www.segaweb.com

SEGA AND DREAMCAST

☺ ☺ ☺ ☺ News, reviews, cheats and much more including

COUNTRY USA chat and letters sections. For the official site with

links and information on the products go to
www.sega-europe.com.

Fantasy league and strategy games

www.dreamleague.com
PLAY FANTASY SPORT

☺☺☺☺☺   Dream League offer fantasy games in five sports;
COUNTRY UK   football, tennis, rugby, golf and cricket. Even
with the sports you can play foreign leagues. It's
easy to register and participate – and it's free.

www.fantasyleague.com
FANTASY FOOTIE

☺☺☺☺   Be a football manager, play for yourself or in a
COUNTRY UK   league, even organise a game for your school.
Get the latest team news on your chosen players
and how they're doing against the rest.
See also **http://uk-fantasyfootball.20m.com/**.

www.primagames.com
PRIMA

☺☺☺   The largest fantasy game publisher offers a site
COUNTRY USA   packed with reviews, demos and articles. You
can also buy a book on virtually every strategy
game. There are also good sections on strategy
games at About.com
http://compstratgames.about.com with links and
background on the games.

Cheats, hints and tips

www.cheatstation.com
THE CHEAT STATION

☺ ☺ ☺ ☺

COUNTRY USA

Select the console or game type that you want a cheat on then drill down the menus until you get the specific game or cheat that you want. There are cheats for almost 7000 games so you should find what you're looking for; but if you can't, check out **www.xcheater.com** who have a smaller selection, but you never know your luck.

Games shops

If you know what game you want then it's probably better to use a price checker such as Kelkoo (**http://uk.kelkoo.com**) to find the best price on the game, they will put you through to the store offering the best all round deal.

If you want to browse then these are considered the best on-line stores for a wide range of games. They are all UK based.

www.chipsworld.co.uk – good for Sega and Nintendo

www.eb.uk.com – Electronic Boutique which is simple with a good loyalty scheme

> **www.gamespot.co.uk** – wide range, lots of info as well
>
> **www.gamesstreet.co.uk** – part of the Streetson-line group, one of the top shops on the internet – good kids section; free delivery in the UK
>
> **www.game-retail.co.uk** – easy-to-use, good range and a loyalty scheme
>
> **www.telegames.co.uk** – around 5000 types of games in stock, covering all makes; also has a bargain section
>
> **www.ukgames.com** – excellent range and good prices.

www.gameswapshop.co.uk

DON'T BUY NEW GAMES, SWAP THEM

☺ ☺ ☺

COUNTRY UK

You have to go through an annoying registration system and loads of adverts but eventually you get to a user-friendly site with a secure swapping system. You can swap games with anyone in the UK who is also registered.

www.wargames.co.uk

WAR GAMES FORUM

☺ ☺ ☺

COUNTRY UK

All you need to know about war-gaming on one site, albeit a slow one. There are links to specialist traders and to every aspect of the game from figurines to books to software.

Games for Mac's

Here are three great sites to help you if you feel restricted by having an Apple Mac.

www.macgamer.com
MAC MAGAZINE

☺☺☺☺
COUNTRY USA

An on-line magazine with all the usual features we've come to expect – news, reviews, links and even a few giveaways. It's all neatly packaged on an attractive web site.

www.macgamefiles.com
MAC GAME FILE LIBRARY

☺☺☺☺
COUNTRY USA

To quote them, 'Macgamefiles.com is THE one-stop source for Macintosh game files. The web site features lively libraries of Macintosh demos, shareware, updaters, tools, add-ons, and more'. And they're right; it's a very good site with some high quality, useful stuff.

www.insidemacgames.com
IMG MAGAZINE

☺☺☺☺
COUNTRY USA

A magazine devoted to Mac Games where you can find the latest demos, updates for the games, loads of shareware games, and news and reviews.

Miscellaneous

www.etch-a-sketch.com
REMEMBER ETCH-A-SKETCH?

☺☺☺☺
COUNTRY USA

For those of you who don't remember back that far Etch-a-Sketch is a rather annoying drawing game; it's been faithfully recreated here and it's still just as difficult to do curves. There are also a few other simple games and some links to kids' games sites.

www.gamedictionary.com
THE GAME DICTIONARY

☺☺☺
COUNTRY USA

Gaming has to have one of the most complicated and sometimes just plain weird vocabularies, so if you're stuck just click on this site and get the definition you need – easy.

Board and card games

www.chess.co.uk
ULTIMATE CHESS

☺☺☺☺
COUNTRY UK

Massive chess site that's got information on the game, news and views, reviews and shopping. There are loads of links to other chess sites and downloads. Check out the similar **www.bcf.ndirect.co.uk** for the British Chess Federation. If you want to play chess try the excellent **www.chessed.com** where you can play others live on-line.

www.gammon.com
BACKGAMMON

☻ ☻ ☻ ☻   If you like backgammon here's the place to start.

COUNTRY USA   There are links to live game playing and masses
of related information. Also check out
www.bkgm.com.

www.msoworld.com
BOARD GAMES, PUZZLES AND QUIZZES

☻ ☻ ☻ ☻   The ultimate site of its type, there are over 100

COUNTRY USA   board games plus masses of quizzes and tests, on
top of that there are over 1000 links to games
sites.

www.scrabble.com
SCRABBLE

☻ ☻   Scrabble addicts start here, unfortunately you

COUNTRY USA   can't play the game on-line, but there are some
good word games on the site such as hangman.
You can also get loads of tips and word lists,
which will help you get to grips with the real
game.

www.thehouseofcards.com
LOADS OF CARD GAMES

☻ ☻ ☻ ☻   Huge number of card games to play and down-

COUNTRY USA   load – there's not much missing here. In addition, there are sections on card tricks, history,
links and word games.

See also www.igames.com and www.pagat.com for alternatives.

www.playsite.com
EASY TO PLAY

☺ ☺ ☺
COUNTRY USA

A collection of straightforward and simple card and board games. There's also a good selection of fantasy games.

www.solitairegames.com
SOLITAIRE

☺ ☺ ☺
COUNTRY USA

On-line playing or download a game on to your PC, there's plenty to choose from and it's quick. There's also a good set of links to other on-line card games.

Crosswords, puzzles and word games

www.cluemaster.com
CROSSWORDS AND WORD PUZZLES

☺ ☺ ☺ ☺
COUNTRY UK

1000 pages of puzzles, word games and crosswords, all free. It's all on a pretty straightforward site, although you have to register to get the best out of it. Check out www.wordcross.net which is a high tech version where you can win prizes as well – if you're over 18.

www.riddler.com
GREAT GRAPHICS, GREAT GAMES

☺ ☺ ☺ ☺ ☺

COUNTRY USA

You have to register to play and pretend to be American (just put some nonsense where it says zip code) but once in you are treated to one of the best-looking sites around. Most of the games are traditional or puzzles and all are entertaining. Once you've become a member you can send out game challenges to friends, unfortunately only Americans can win the prizes.

Quizzes and general knowledge

www.trivialpursuitonline.com
TEST YOUR KNOWLEDGE

☺ ☺ ☺ ☺

COUNTRY USA

This site is a site for trivial pursuit addicts everywhere, you have to download the program but once that's done and you've chosen your character you can play others at the game.

For alternatives check out these sites:

www.coolquiz.com – several different types of quiz from sports to movies and quotes, nice wacky design. (USA)

www.quiz.co.uk – 1000 questions in several unusual categories including kids, nature, food and sport (UK)

www.trivia.co.uk – excellent for fans of soap operas, plus pop, movies and much more; you have to register (UK)

www.test.com – mainly serious tests but you can find out your IQ, find out how creative you are and when you visit the family section take tests on entertainment and sports amongst others. You have to pay for some of the tests. (USA)

www.thinks.com

FUN AND GAMES FOR PLAYFUL BRAINS

☺ ☺ ☺ ☺

COUNTRY USA

Massive collection of games, puzzles and quizzes with something for everyone organised into over 20 categories. It's easy to navigate and free to use – unless you take into consideration the advertising.

www.mensa.org.uk

THE HIGH IQ SOCIETY

☺ ☺ ☺

COUNTRY UK

Mensa only admit people who pass their high IQ test – see if you've got what it takes. The site has a few free tests and, if eligible, you can join the club.

Greetings cards

Send your friends virtual greetings cards; you know they'll love you for it!

www.bluemountain.com
E-CARDS FOR FREE

☺☺☺☺☺

COUNTRY USA

Blue Mountain has thousands of cards for every occasion; it's easy-to-use and free. There are all sorts of extras you can build in like music, cartoons and even voice messages. Really annoying music goes with it though! If you can't find what you want here then check out **www.egreetings.com**, which is similar but has a different selection, or the slushy and very American **www.greeting-cards.com**.

www.nextcard.co.uk
3D CARDS

☺☺☺

COUNTRY UK

Send three-dimensional cards using this site, there are great pictures of animals, sunsets and mountain scenery to choose from.

www.madopolis.com
GIVE MONEY TO CHARITY AT NO COST TO YOU

☺☺☺

COUNTRY UK

At Madopolis for every e-card you send their sponsor sends 2p to the charity you choose. There's a good selection with a wide range of good quality pictures. It's easy-to-use but a little slow.

Homework

Unfortunately homework is inescapable, but here's where to go for the best help. This section is divided up into school subject areas, but also includes subjects such as nature, space, and museums. Don't limit your search too much though, as even if you need something specific it's also worth checking out the general homework sites, as they are packed with info. Remember that many sites are American so although the information is OK, it may be biased towards their curriculum.

General homework help sites A-Z

www.a-levels.co.uk

A-LEVELS – A DODDLE?

☺☺☺   Lots of promise and plenty of detail on the key

COUNTRY UK   subjects, but it's still being developed. Looks
           good though.

www.bbc.co.uk/education

GET EQUIPPED FOR LIFE

☺☺☺   Great for homework, with information on all

COUNTRY UK   the BBC's education-related programs and activi-
           ties. Watch out though, as each section tends to
           be tied to a particular program rather than

subject. There are also sections in French,
Italian, German and Spanish.

www.bigchalk.com
HOMEWORK CENTRAL

☺☺☺☺   Click on the student's area and you get put
COUNTRY USA   through to Homework Central, which has links
to lots of excellent information, web sites and
subjects. There are also games, competitions and
quizzes if you get bored.

www.cln.org/int_expert.html
ASK AN EXPERT

☺☺☺☺   This site lists almost a hundred sites by subject
COUNTRY USA   and all provide an expert to answer your homework question – what a doddle! Big American
bias though.

www.educate.org.uk
EDUCATE YOURSELF

☺☺☺   It will be good when it's finished – honest! At the
COUNTRY UK   moment, take advantage of the web directory
which is really good and covers virtually every
school subject.

www.eduweb.co.uk
THE INTERNET SERVICE FOR TEACHERS AND PUPILS

☺☺☺   With EduWeb you are getting access to a
COUNTRY UK   massive amount of data for use on homework,
advice on how to study and use of the

curriculum and a net pen pals service. There's also tons of stuff for teachers and parents such as advice on projects and where to find the best school. It's great but costs £49 a year!

www.en.eun.org
THE EUROPEAN SCHOOL NET

☺☺☺☺
COUNTRY BELGIUM

Click on the word 'pupils' and you get through to the interesting bit, well useful bit anyway. Here you'll find links to other useful web sites, pen pals and the latest news – great for Euro-homework.

www.enchantedlearning.com
FROM APES TO WHALES

☺☺☺
COUNTRY USA

It's messy, uncool and some of it is aimed at young kids, but there's loads of good information hidden away, especially on nature. Use the search engine to find what you need.

www.gcse.com
GCSE ANSWERS

☺☺☺☺
COUNTRY UK

This site that has tests and past papers for English and Maths GCSE exams, it's building fast with some stuff available on other exam subjects too. Included are tips on how to get good results and information on the various examination boards.

www.homeworkelephant.free-online.co.uk
LET THE ELEPHANT HELP

☺ ☺ ☺ ☺   A totally brilliant site with some 700 links aimed

COUNTRY UK   at helping you achieve great results, there's help
with specific subjects, hints & tips, help for
parents and teachers. The site is constantly being
updated, so it's worth checking regularly.

www.homeworkhigh.co.uk
LEARN WITH CHANNEL 4

☺ ☺ ☺ ☺ ☺   Split into 6 sections: History, Geography,

COUNTRY UK   Science, Maths, English and News, this is one of
the cool homework sites. You can send questions
to experts, retrieve lots of info and you can chat
with fellow homework sufferers. Excellent.

www.learn.com
SMARTEST PLACE ON THE WEB

☺ ☺ ☺ ☺   Once you've registered (very easy) you're enti-

COUNTRY US   tled to free access to all the on-line courses,
which range from how to bake spicy fries to
how to convert Centigrade into Fahrenheit. It's
not easy to find specific facts, but if you have a
project to do there's bound to be something here
to help you out.

www.learnfree.co.uk
EDUCATION FOR ALL

☺☺☺☺☺ Although it is primarily aimed at parents, there
COUNTRY UK is masses of useful stuff here for every age from
pre-school to A-level. It looks daunting, but take
your time and search out your subject. It's hard
to believe they can pack so much into one site.

www.lineone.net/learning/
A COMPREHENSIVE EDUCATION

☺☺☺ A good starting point for information on most
COUNTRY UK subjects in the curriculum at all levels. The navi-
gation is clear and the links useful.

www.ngfl.gov.uk
THE NATIONAL GRID FOR LEARNING

☺☺☺ The official government education site, it's got
COUNTRY UK sections for every aspect of learning. There's
something for everyone, whatever your needs,
along with details about the key museums,
galleries and libraries. There is also a section on
education in the Commonwealth.

www.pinchbeck.com
ANSWERS TO HOMEWORK, FREE

☺☺☺ This huge database is one of the biggest on-line
COUNTRY USA homework sites, with some 600 links. In theory,
homework was never so easy, however, to British
eyes, it can seem a bit odd.

www.samlearning.com
EXAM REVISION
☺☺☺☺☺
COUNTRY UK

SAM stands for self-assessment and marking, and on this brilliant site you can do just that. It has mock exams covering every major subject and key stage including GCSEs and A-levels. There are top tips on taking exams and the chance to win some great prizes when you register.

www.schoolzone.co.uk
UK's TOP EDUCATIONAL SEARCH ENGINE
☺☺☺☺☺
COUNTRY UK

With over 30,000 sites and bits of resource, all rated and checked by teachers, schoolzone provides masses of useful information. There is free software to download, plus homework help, career advice, teacher support (they do need it apparently) and much more. Don't be put off by the confusing layout; it's worth sticking with.

www.startribune.com/homework
HOMEWORK ON THE BRAIN
☺☺☺☺
COUNTRY USA

Just click on the right bit of the brain on the homepage and you get put through to the subject you're after. There are lots of links to other learning web sites plus bags of tips and information. You can even e-mail a question; they try to reply within 24 hours.

National Curriculum

www.dfee.gov.uk/nc
NATIONAL CURRICULUM REVEALED

☺☺☺☺   Very detailed explanation of the National
COUNTRY UK   Curriculum and what's expected of you. Scary!
For more information on the national curriculum see **www.qca.org.uk**. For information on the Scottish education system see **www.sqa.org.uk**.

Facts, encyclopaedias, dictionaries and directories

www.about.com
IT'S ABOUT INFORMATION

☺☺☺☺☺   Easy-to-use and great for beginners who are
COUNTRY USA   learning to search for info on the net. There are experts to help you find what you need every step of the way. About offers tons of stuff on a wide range of topics from the arts to sciences, there's even a section on shopping.

www.comptons.com
COMPTONS ON-LINE ENCYCLOPAEDIA

☺☺☺   An OK encyclopaedia with a really good search
COUNTRY USA   facility that makes it easy to find what you're looking for. Answers have an American rather than a UK bias.

www.dk.com
DORLING KINDERSLEY PUBLISHING

☺☺☺☺☺
COUNTRY UK

Offers on DK books and CD Roms is reason enough to visit this totally brilliant site, but you can also get access to the excellent Eyewitness Encyclopaedia which has 2 million words and 40,000 pictures. The interactive tests section on the key GCSE subjects is great.

http://encarta.msn.com
THE ENCARTA ENCYCLOPAEDIA

☺☺☺
COUNTRY USA

Even though the complete thing is only available to buy, there is access to over 16,000 articles and reference notes via the concise version. It's fast and easy-to-use.

www.eb.com
ENCYCLOPAEDIA BRITANNICA

☺☺☺
COUNTRY USA

You can either trial this famous encyclopaedia for 14 days (after that you have to buy it) or go to **www.britannica.com** and get virtually the whole thing anyway. The web site is confusing at first but it does have a really good search facility. It brings up not only your answer but related web sites and other information too. It's worth checking out the visually similar, but newsier **www.infoplease.com** as well.

www.ehow.com
HOW TO...

☺☺☺ Step-by-step instructions on how to do just
COUNTRY USA about anything. Just type in your request and off
you go; it's useful for annoying projects.

www.encyclopedia.com
FREE ENCYCLOPAEDIA

☺☺☺☺ No 14 day trial, no catch just a straightforward,
COUNTRY USA easy-to-use encyclopaedia. The answers are short
and to the point with links to more information
if you need it. There's also a section where you
can ask an expert.

www.funkandwagnalls.com
THINK SMART, THINK MORE, USE THIS

☺☺☺ An encyclopaedia, dictionary and atlas all rolled
COUNTRY USA into one. It doesn't have as much information as
some of the other sites, but it's easy-to-use and it
saves you changing sites too often. You could
check out www.worldbookonline.com which is
good but only free for 30 days, which is a bit
rich considering there's so much free stuff about.

www.ipl.org
THE INTERNET PUBLIC LIBRARY

☺☺☺☺☺ Another excellent place to find facts, there are
COUNTRY USA articles on a vast range of subjects. There's a
section for teenagers and if you go into the

'youth' section there's loads of stuff to help with the homework. If the library can't help with your request, there is usually a link to take you to an alternative web site. See also **www.libraryspot.com**.

www.letsfindout.com
KNOWLEDGE ADVENTURE

☺ ☺ ☺ ☺
COUNTRY USA

This encyclopaedia is more fun to use than most, it looks good and it's got a cool search facility. The down side is that the information is really biased to America. **www.learn2.com** is also worth a visit.

www.onelook.com
OVER 600 DICTIONARIES!

☺ ☺ ☺ ☺
COUNTRY USA

629 to be precise, with almost 2.5 million words, you should be able to find what you're looking for here – in 5 languages too. And it's quick.

See also **www.m-w.com/netdict.htm**, which is Websters dictionary and **www.dictionary.com**.

www.thesaurus.com
IF YOU CAN'T FIND THE RIGHT WORD

☺ ☺ ☺
COUNTRY USA

Based on Roget's thesaurus this site will help you to find alternative words.

www.plumbdesign.com/thesaurus/
THE VISUAL THESAURUS
☺☺☺☺

COUNTRY USA

If you get bored looking up words or looking for alternative meanings for words in the usual way, then check out the Visual Thesaurus at Plumb Design. It's fun to use if a bit weird.

www.refdesk.com
THE BEST SINGLE SOURCE FOR FACTS – JUST DON'T YAWN!
☺☺☺☺

COUNTRY USA

Information and links to just about anything, its all very serious (even the 'just for fun' bit), but then it's won loads of awards and it always seems to help you get the answer.

www.studyweb.com
SITES, SITES AND MORE SITES
☺☺☺☺

COUNTRY USA

A humungous directory of over 128,000 web sites, many related to education, but general interest subjects such as sport and entertainment are covered too. If you are looking for info, start by clicking on 'Reference' or just use the brilliant search engine.

www.spartacus.schoolnet.co.uk
SPARTACUS ENCYCLOPAEDIA
☺☺☺

COUNTRY UK

A good history based encyclopaedia with excellent links to other educational and factual web sites. The difficulty is in finding what you really want as it's not exactly well-designed.

www.whsmith.co.uk
REVISE AND SHOP

☺☺☺☺
COUNTRY UK

You can get free access to the Hutchinson Encyclopaedia, which has 18,000 entries and is good for GCSE and National Curriculum studies. In the Education Zone you'll find exam help, revision guides and you can even get involved in a virtual 'school debate'.

The arts

The following sections highlight the best sites for galleries, museums, exhibitions, and how to get the best clip-art to make your work look great.

www.artlex.com
THE VISUAL ARTS DICTIONARY

☺☺☺
COUNTRY USA

There are over 3000 definitions of art-related terms with links to other sites and articles. However it can be very slow and some of the links aren't reliable, but it's still worth a try.

The major British museums and galleries

www.tate.org.uk
BRILLIANT GALLERY SITE

☺☺☺☺
COUNTRY UK

The Tate has loads of good quality pictures. It's divided into several sections: one for each main gallery (including the Tate Modern) with details about what's on and what's coming; and the collection, which can be browsed or searched by artist. The shop sells art-related stuff, but you must order by fax! Warning – it can be a bit too serious.

www.nationalgallery.org.uk
THE NATIONAL COLLECTION OF WESTERN EUROPEAN PAINTING

☺ ☺ ☺ ☺

COUNTRY UK

Similar to the serious style of the Tate site, the collection has very good quality pictures with notes on each one. Also covered is what's on and when, what's new and coming, plus information on the gallery – how to get there etc. There's a good search facility too but no on-line shop. For all the Scottish National Galleries go to www.natgalscot.ac.uk.

www.britishmuseum.ac.uk
BUILDING THE BRITISH MUSEUM

☺ ☺ ☺ ☺

COUNTRY UK

Another great site for getting your homework done, it's all about world cultures, with really good pictures and information. The on-line shop stocks a selection of gifts and goods based on museum artefacts. Delivery in the UK is £3.95.

www.npg.org.uk
THE NATIONAL PORTRAIT GALLERY

☺ ☺ ☺ ☺
COUNTRY UK

With an amazing 10,000 pictures on view, this is one of the biggest on-line galleries. It shows the most influential characters in British history portrayed by artists of their time. You can search by sitter or artist, and buy the print. The on-line shop offers options on print size, framing and delivery, including overseas.

www.vam.ac.uk
VICTORIA AND ALBERT

☺ ☺ ☺
COUNTRY UK

The V&A is the largest museum for decorative arts and this cool site reflects that, but it's surprisingly lacking in information. Go into the explorer section for the current on-line displays and exhibitions, go into The Crypt for the archive.

Museums and galleries abroad

www.moma.org
MUSEUM OF MODERN ART IN NEW YORK

☺ ☺ ☺ ☺
COUNTRY USA

Really nice-looking site which is split into six major areas, the main ones being: The Collection, with a selection of the best paintings; What's On and Educational Support aimed at teachers and pupils. The on-line store is excellent for weird gifts but delivery to the UK is expensive.

www.metmuseum.org
THE METROPOLITAN MUSEUM OF ART IN NEW YORK

☺☺☺☺ A new and very cool site with lots of great ideas.

COUNTRY USA You can view any one of 3,500 exhibits, become a member, or visit a special exhibition. Homework aside, the shop is the best bit with lots of groovy gifts. Delivery cost to the UK depends on how much you spend.

www.uffizi.firenze.it/welcome.html
THE UFFIZI GALLERY IN FLORENCE

☺☺☺☺ Check out the fantastic quality of the paintings.

COUNTRY ITALY Finding your way round is easy and quicker than most too. There is also gallery information and a tour.

www.louvre.fr
FRANCE'S TREASURE HOUSE

☺☺☺ Similar to the UK's National Gallery site, you

COUNTRY FRANCE can take a virtual tour, view the collection, and learn about its history. The shop has some interesting stuff but delivery to the UK is about £7.

Clip-art

www.clipart.com
THE PLACE TO START IF YOU NEED CLIP-ART

☺☺☺☺ Links to over 500 clip-art sites but using the

COUNTRY USA good search facility, you should quickly find the perfect image. Although huge, this site is low on information. Many linked sites have free art for use, otherwise cost varies depending on what you want. You can also try the very similar **www.clipart.net** as well.

English – language and literature (including the classics)

http://classics.mit.edu
THE INTERNET CLASSICS ARCHIVE
☺☺☺☺ An excellent site for researching into the classics,
COUNTRY USA it's easy-to-use and fast, with more than enough information for homework, whatever the level.

www.pantheon.org
ENCYCLOPAEDIA OF MYTHS AND LEGENDS
☺☺☺☺☺ If you really don't know your Xena from your
COUNTRY USA Hercules then here's the place to come. Featuring all your usual unicorns and dragons plus a few characters you've probably never heard of, it's fast, easy-to-use and well written.

www.edunet.com/english/grammar/
FROM ADVERBS TO VERBS
☺☺☺ Everything you need to know about how to use
COUNTRY UK English.

www.acronymfinder.com
WHAT DO THOSE INITIALS STAND FOR?
☺ ☺ ☺
COUNTRY USA

If you don't know your MP from your MP3 here's where to go. With over 150,000 acronyms you should find what you're looking for.

www.symbols.com
☺ ☺ ☺
COUNTRY USA

Here you can find the meaning of over 2500 symbols, with articles on their history.

www.bibliomania.com
THE CLASSICS ON-LINE
☺ ☺ ☺ ☺
COUNTRY USA

Bibliomania has over 70 classic novels, the complete works of Shakespeare, plus many great reference works available for you to print or download. You can search the entire site for quotes or for a specific book.

www.shakespeare.sk/
FARTUOUS AND CUNNING
☺ ☺ ☺
COUNTRY USA

This is really a straightforward site featuring the complete writings of Shakespeare, including biographical details, and a glossary explaining the language of the time.

www.eserver.org
THE ENGLISH SERVER
☺ ☺ ☺
COUNTRY USA

A boring site to look at, however, it's got a vast amount of data about almost every cultural topic. There are some 20,000 texts, articles and essays available.

Foreign languages

http://dictionaries.travlang.com
FOREIGN LANGUAGE DICTIONARIES

☺☺☺☺☺

COUNTRY USA

There are 16 language dictionaries on this site, just select the dictionary you want, and then type in the word or sentence to be translated – it couldn't be simpler. Originally aimed at the traveller, but whatever, it's very useful for homework too.

http://babelfish.altavista.digital.com
TRANSLATE ANYTHING

☺☺☺☺

COUNTRY USA

Just type in the sentence, select the language and in a few seconds you get the translation back. Great for chat up lines and homework alike. You can even translate whole documents but get permission to download the software first.

Geography

www.ntu.edu.sg/library/stat/statdata.htm
STATISTICS AND MORE STATISTICS

☺☺☺☺

COUNTRY USA

Free information and statistics about every world economy, not that easy-to-use at first, but it's all there. For the UK only go to **www.statistics.gov.uk**.

www.atlapedia.com
THE WORLD IN BOTH PICTURES AND NUMBERS

☺ ☺ ☺

COUNTRY USA

Contains full colour political and physical maps of the world with statistics and very detailed information on each country. It can be very slow, so you need patience, but the end results are worth it.

www.millennium-map.com
THE MILLENNIUM MAP

☺ ☺ ☺

COUNTRY UK

Just type in your postcode or town and up pops a satellite image of the area, or by downloading a piece of software you can literally browse the UK. You can also get historical information on the area as well. Some areas are not covered yet.

www.50states.com
GOOD OLD US OF A

☺ ☺ ☺

COUNTRY USA

A site with basic info on each US state and major cities, it's well illustrated with maps, links and biographical information on famous residents.

http://volcano.und.nodak.edu/vw.html
VOLCANO WORLD

☺ ☺ ☺ ☺

COUNTRY USA

Everything you need to know about the volcano, from what's currently erupting, to detailed information on how they work. They have some great pictures. Younger kids can try **www.surfnetkids.com/volcano.htm**.

www.civeng.carleton.ca/cgi-bin/quakes/

NATIONAL EARTHQUAKE INFORMATION CENTRE

☺☺☺☺ The world data centre for seismology in Denver
COUNTRY USA logs all the world's earthquakes; there's also
earthquake information, maps and links to other
web sites.

History

ww.thehistorychannel.com

THE BEST SEARCH IN HISTORY

☺☺☺☺ Excellent for revision or just a good read. The
COUNTRY USA History Channel provides a site that is packed
with information, search by key word or time-
line, and get biographical information, speeches,
by date and by subject. It's fast and easy to get
carried away once you start your search.

www.historytoday.com

WORLD'S LEADING HISTORY MAGAZINE

☺☺☺ Contains some excellent articles from the maga-
COUNTRY UK zine, but the most useful bit for homework
purposes is the related links section, which offers
over 100 links to other history sites.

www.ukans.edu/history/VL

THE VIRTUAL WORLD HISTORY LIBRARY

☺☺☺☺ Those folks at the University of Kansas love
COUNTRY USA their history and have put together a huge

library, organised by country and historical
period. It's got an easy-to-use search engine too.

www.thehistorynet.com
MODERN HISTORY AMERICAN STYLE

☺☺☺☺
COUNTRY USA

This site is excellent for the World Wars, technology and American history. It brings history to
life by using the eyewitness accounts of people
who were actually there. There's also a good
archive with some pieces on British history too.
You could also try **www.historyplace.com**,
which is similar and has some great historic
photos. There's also **www.ibiscom.com** who
have a large catalogue of historical recollections
both ancient and modern.

www.biography.com
FIND OUT ABOUT ANYONE WHO WAS ANYONE

☺☺☺☺
COUNTRY USA

Over 25,000 biographical references and some
2,500 videos make this site a great option if you
need to find out about someone in a hurry. There
are special features such as a book club and a
magazine, there is a shop but, at time of going to
press, they didn't ship to the UK.

http://royal.gov.uk/
THE ROYAL FAMILY

☺☺☺☺
COUNTRY UK

No not the TV show. This is the official web site
for the British Monarchy; it has biographies of
the current royals and a history of both English

and Scottish thrones. There are profiles of the
major Kings and Queens and historic speeches.
For other web sites on the Royals try
www.royalfamily.com which covers the whole
world and **www.camelotintl.com/royal/.**
www.eurohistory.com has loads of information
on the European Monarchies and their history.

www.british-forces.com
HISTORY OF THE BRITISH ARMED FORCES
☺☺☺　　　Excellent on the World Wars, conflicts, medals,
COUNTRY UK　statistics and recommended sites. It's not very
　　　　　well-designed but there's loads of information
　　　　　there.

www.tudortimes.com
HEY NONNY NONNY
☺☺☺　　　News of Tudor times (1485 to 1603) written in
COUNTRY USA　the style of a newspaper, it's light-hearted and
　　　　　gives a good feel about what it was like to live
　　　　　during that time. It's a shame that it takes ages
　　　　　to download, and has such annoying music.

http://ireland.iol.ie/~coolmine/typ/romans/intro.html
THE ROMANS
☺☺☺　　　　　Discover what the Romans got up to here. It's a
COUNTRY IRELAND fairly basic design but the information is good.
　　　　　The BBC has a good Romans page on
　　　　　www.bbc.co.uk/education/romans.

www.eyelid.co.uk,
ANCIENT EGYPT

☺ ☺ ☺ ☺
COUNTRY UK

Mark Millmore must love Egyptians, his site has a wide range of information on Egypt, with features on pyramids, pharaohs, and hieroglyphics. There's also games, screensavers and good links to related sites. If you can't find what you're looking for here, then try **http://guardians.net/egypt/**, which is high on info but has an annoying design.

www.domesdaybook.co.uk
THE DOMESDAY BOOK

☺ ☺ ☺ ☺
COUNTRY UK

Search by county or town and you get the Domesday Book entry, with notes explaining the language of the time and what the names mean. There's also stuff on who owned what and how they lived in the 11th Century.

www.regia.org
ANGLO SAXONS, NORMANS AND VIKINGS

☺ ☺ ☺
COUNTRY UK

Devoted to early English history, this site is well-designed and well worth a look if you have a project to do. Visit the village of Wichamstow to find out about how life was lived a thousand years ago.

http://viking.no
GET TO KNOW THE VIKINGS
☺ ☺ ☺ ☺   Find out what they were really like from the
COUNTRY NORWAY   Vikings themselves – well the Norwegians
anyway. Easy-to-use and doesn't miss much.

www.castlesontheweb.com
CASTLES AND MORE
☺ ☺ ☺ ☺   If you need any info on castles, this is the site for
COUNTRY USA   you. Started by a castle nut, there are hundreds
of links to web sites relating to castles, their
history and the people who lived in them. All are
rated. Good for information on heraldry and
mediaeval life too.

www.museumofcostume.co.uk
COSTUME THROUGH THE AGES
☺ ☺ ☺ ☺   Excellent site showing how the design of
COUNTRY UK   costume has changed through the ages. There's a
virtual tour and links to other museums based in
Bath.

Nature and the environment

www.panda.org
THE WORLD WIDE FUND FOR NATURE
☺ ☺ ☺ ☺   Information on projects designed to save the
COUNTRY UK   world's endangered species by protecting their
environment. You can: find out about the charity

and how to contribute; visit the photo, video and
art galleries; go to the Just for Kids section, where
you'll find quizzes and virtual wildlife tours; then
there's much more info in the archives.

An American organisation called the National
Wildlife Fund has a similar excellent site at
www.nwf.org.

www.nhm.ac.uk
THE NATURAL HISTORY MUSEUM

☺☺☺☺☺ An easy-to-use web site that covers everything
COUNTRY UK from ants to eclipses. You can get the latest
news, check out exhibitions, take a tour or
watch the live ant-cast. Also has details on the
collections and contacts for answers to specific
questions.

www.naturenet.net
COUNTRYSIDE, NATURE AND CONSERVATION

☺☺☺☺ Ignore the annoying graphics and you'll
COUNTRY UK find loads of stuff about nature in the UK.
Their interests include: countryside law,
upkeep of nature reserves, voluntary work,
education and environmental news. You
can also search the site for specific things
and there is a good set of links to related
sites. See also **www.wildlifetrust.org.uk**
and **www.uksafari.com.**

www.foe.co.uk
FRIENDS OF THE EARTH
☺☺☺☺

COUNTRY UK

Not as dull as you'd think, this site offers a stack of info on food, pollution, green power, protecting wildlife in your area plus the latest campaign news.

www.arkive.org.uk
ARCHIVE OF ENDANGERED SPECIES
☺☺☺☺

COUNTRY UK

Sponsored by the Wildscreen Trust (www.wildscreen.org.uk) this site will eventually catalogue and picture all the world's endangered species. You can help by donating pictures and film.

www.envirolink.org
THE ON-LINE ENVIRONMENTAL COMMUNITY
☺☺☺☺

COUNTRY USA

A mega-site focused on personal involvement in environment issues. There are over 25 sections with the key ones being: direct action, animal rights, what to boycott, a reference library, business and the environment, jobs and environmental events. There is also a good search facility on environment-related topics.

Real campaigners go to Greenpeace site **www.greenpeace.org** where you can find out about their latest activities and how to get involved.

www.planetdiary.com
A RECORD OF WHAT'S REALLY HAPPENING ON THE PLANET

☺ ☺ ☺ ☺

COUNTRY USA

Every week Planetdiary monitors and records world events in geological, astronomical, meteorological, biological and environmental terms and relays them back via this web site. It's done by showing an icon on a map of the world, which you then click on to find out more. Although very informative, a visit can leave you a little depressed.

www.bbc.co.uk/nature
BBC WILDLIFE

☺ ☺ ☺ ☺

COUNTRY UK

A totally brilliant nature offering, with sections on key wildlife programmes and animal groups, the information is good and enhanced by view clips. Also visit **www.bbcwild.com**, the commercial side of the BBC wildlife unit with over 100,000 wildlife images available to buy. It's aimed at commercial organisations but plans to offer pictures for personal use at £15 each. It is a great place to browse for the amazing images in the premium selection.

www.insects.org
VERY COOL BUGS – YUK!

☺ ☺ ☺

COUNTRY USA

Everything you want to know about insects but were afraid to ask. There's an explanation about each type, how they interact with humans, with pictures and links to other insect sites.

More for enthusiasts than anything, but there may be something here for homework.

Information technology

www.technologyindex.com
TECHNOLOGY EDUCATION INDEX

☺☺☺☺　On the face of it this is a shop selling the latest
COUNTRY UK　gadgets and gizmos, but click on 'Exam Help' and you get a section that helps you find sites or web pages on subjects such as electronics, design, textiles and much more.

www.whatis.com
I.T. ENCYCLOPAEDIA

☺☺☺☺☺　A totally massive database, whether you use the
COUNTRY USA　search engine or browse by category, this site is excellent for information on I.T. You need to register to get the best out of it.

www.netdictionary.com.
NET JARGON

☺☺☺☺　Sound like you know what you're talking
COUNTRY USA　about or just get less confused about technical terminology, either way the net dictionary helps you get by.

Maths

www.maths-help.co.uk
E-MAIL YOUR MATHS PROBLEMS

☺☺☺☺

COUNTRY UK

Send your queries to maths-help and they'll e-mail you back the answers in a couple of days. You can also visit the knowledge bank to see past queries and answers.

www.anglia.co.uk/education/mathsnet
MATHS NET

☺☺☺☺

COUNTRY UK

Great for not only maths but technical information too, there are sections on schoolwork as well as games, software, calculators and an excellent section on shapes and geometry. You can also go to the Geometry Centre at www.geom.umn.edu.

www.argonet.co.uk/oundlesch/mlink.html
OUNDLE SCHOOL

☺☺☺

COUNTRY UK

Oundle School has put together a really good list of maths web sites, which includes games, statistics, resources, associations and magazines.

www.c3.lanl.gov/mega-math/
MEGA MATHEMATICS

☺☺☺

COUNTRY USA

It's a bit confusing to use, but once you've got the hang of it the Los Alamos National Laboratories site is really useful with explanations of all the different aspects of maths and links to other sites.

Music

www.listensmart.com/learn/music/
LEARN ABOUT MUSIC

☺☺☺☺☺

COUNTRY USA

Excellent overview of most major musical instruments, plus links to related web sites. It also has descriptions on the general structure of music, as well as sound demos, history and much more. Check out **www.learnmusic.iwarp.com/main.html**, which is a British site that also has good information.

www.dragnet.com.au/~donovan/mb/music.html
MUSICIANSHIP BASICS

☺☺

COUNTRY AUSTRALIA

Designed by teachers for use in schools, it covers basic music skills to an advanced level. It costs £26 for the whole course; you can get a free demo from the site.

www.happynote.com/music/learn.html

LEARN MUSIC WITH A GAME

☻☻☻   Download the game, which helps you learn the
COUNTRY USA   basics of music. The more you learn and the
better you get, the higher the score.

Politics

http://open.gov.co.uk

FOR GOVERNMENT INFORMATION

☻☻☻☻☻   A massive web site devoted to the workings of
COUNTRY UK   the British government. It is a superb resource if
you want to know anything official both at a
national and a local level. Use the index or the
search facility to navigate, as it's easy to get side-
tracked. The top features are a list of top 10 web
sites, monarchy section, a download section and
a feedback service. Also check out
www.ukstate.com, which is a great site devoted
to opening up on government information.

For info on each major party go to:
www.labour.org.uk
www.conservative-party.org.uk
www.libdems.org.uk

If you need to know anything about how the
European Parliament works and have a good
yawn at the same time go to **www.europarl.eu.int**

For information on the goings on at the House of Commons, visit **www.parliament.uk/commons/hsecom.htm.**

Go here for the United Nations – **www.un.org.**

Religion

www.omsakthi.org/religions.html
INFORMATION ON ALL THE WORLD'S RELIGIONS

☺ ☺ ☺ ☺
COUNTRY USA
This site provides a clear description of each religion including values and basic beliefs, with links to books on each one.

www.ajbird.demon.co.uk
ULTIMATE COLLECTION OF RE RESOURCES

☺ ☺ ☺
COUNTRY UK
Slow, difficult to use and a bit heavy going, but it's got loads of information and links to relevant sites if you persevere with it. Go to the Lesson Plan Warehouse for explanations of the various religions.

Science

www.abc.net.au/science/
ABC SCIENCE

☺ ☺ ☺
COUNTRY AUSTRALIA
Australia's version of the BBC has it's own fun science site which is easy-to-use and has lots of information. Most of it is linked to programmes we don't see but that seems to make it all the more interesting.

www.brain.com

WELCOME TO THE BRAIN

☺☺☺☺

COUNTRY USA

The Brain is about the science of the body with articles and features on how it all works. Really good design combined with a great search facility.

www.discovery.com

THE DISCOVERY CHANNEL

☺☺☺☺

COUNTRY USA

A brill site for science and nature lovers, it's inspiring as well as educational. Order the weekly newsletter, get information on the latest discoveries, read features on pets, space, travel, lifestyle and school.

www.ems.psu.edu/~fraser/BadScience.html

BAD SCIENCE TEACHER – BEWARE

☺☺

COUNTRY USA

This site was designed to show up 'well under-stood phenomena which are persistently presented incorrectly by teachers'. It's a shame that it's so badly designed.

www.exploratorium.edu

THE EXPLORATORIUM

☺☺☺☺

COUNTRY USA

San Francisco's science museum has a very cool site, full of info and things to do. It has special features on aspects of science from how to dissect a cow's eye to simple experiments you can do at home, as well as links to related sites.

www.howstuffworks.com
HOW STUFF REALLY WORKS

☺☺☺☺☺

COUNTRY USA

Easy-to-use and fascinating, there are 27 sections ranging from the obvious engines and technology, through to food and the weather. The current top 10 section features the latest answers to the questions of the day.

http://library.advanced.org/11924/
THE WIZARD'S LAB

☺☺☺

COUNTRY USA

The friendly wizard helps you through the lab where you can learn about things like motion, light and electricity. All very Harry Potter.

www.madsci.org
THE LAB THAT NEVER SLEEPS

☺☺☺☺

COUNTRY USA

Science and fun in one place! You can ask the mad scientist a question, browse the links list or check out the archives in the library.

www.newscientist.com
NEW SCIENTIST MAGAZINE

☺☺☺☺

COUNTRY USA

Don't be put off by the fuddy-duddy image; this is much better than the usual on-line magazines because it's simultaneously fun and serious. It's easy to search the site or browse through back features – the Even More Bizarre bit is great. For a more traditional science magazine site go to Popular Science at **www.popsci.com**, great for information on the latest gadgets.

www.sciseek.com

ON-LINE RESOURCE FOR SCIENCE AND NATURE

☺☺☺☺ A good place to start, Sciseek lists over 1,000
COUNTRY USA sites on everything from agriculture to chemistry
to health to physics, each site is reviewed and
you can leave your comments too.

www.sciencemuseum.org.uk

THE SCIENCE MUSEUM

☺☺ Click on 'learn and teach' and you get through
COUNTRY UK to the education section – there's not much there
though, it's geared to getting schools to visit the
museum, which is an opportunity missed. It's
also very slow.

www.webelements.com

THE PERIODIC TABLE

☺☺☺ Neatly laid out, just click on the relevant
COUNTRY UK element and up pops all the information. Easy.

http://whyfiles.news.wisc.edu/index.html

THE SCIENCE BEHIND THE NEWS

☺☺☺ The Why Files explain the science behind the
COUNTRY USA latest news stories and they've got a great
archive of previous stories too. There's a cool
images section, where you have er... cool images
and a search engine for when you need to look
things up.

Space

www.space.com
MAKING SPACE POPULAR

☺ ☺ ☺ ☺ ☺   There's the latest news, mission reports, technol-
COUNTRY USA   ogy, history, personalities, a kids section and
plenty of pictures. The science section explores
the planets and earth. You can buy goods at the
space shop with delivery cost dependent on
purchase.

www.seds.org/billa/tnp/
THE NINE PLANETS

☺ ☺ ☺ ☺ ☺   A multi-media tour of the nine planets, amazing
COUNTRY USA   photography, and interesting facts combined
with good writing. View the moon or the earth
from virtually any angle, day or night from
www.fourmilab.ch/earthview/vplanet.html.
There's also the brilliant
www.inconstantmoon.com which features
illustrated trips to the moon every night.

www.nasa.gov/
THE OFFICIAL NASA SITE

☺ ☺ ☺   This huge site has loads of information on the
COUNTRY USA   US National Aeronautical and Space
Administration. There are sections on each
NASA location, launch timings, news and
project updates plus links to their specialist sites

such the Hubble Space Telescope. There's a kids
section too. For Britain's place in space go to
www.bnsc.gov.uk.

www.nauts.com
☺☺☺☺☺ THE ASTRONAUT CONNECTION

COUNTRY USA If you want to learn about what astronauts get
up to then it's all here.

www.setiathome.ssl.berkeley.edu/
GET IN TOUCH WITH AN ALIEN

☺☺☺ To borrow the official site description

COUNTRY USA 'SETI@home is a scientific experiment that uses
internet-connected computers in the Search for
Extraterrestrial Intelligence (SETI). You can
participate by running a free program that
downloads and analyses radio telescope data'.

Nothing to do with homework, but you could
be the first to talk to an alien. Get permission
before downloading the program.

Movies

All you need to know about films and film stars including where to get the best deals on DVDs and videos. For information on film stars also check out the celebrities section on page 29.

http://uk.imdb.com
INTERNET MOVIE DATABASE

ʊ ʊ ʊ ʊ ʊ

COUNTRY USA

The best and most organised movie database on the internet, it's very easy-to-use and every film buffs dream. In 'What's Hot' check out new releases, get the latest movie news and reviews, do the quizzes, leave a review or take up a recommendation. There's also a handy 'if you liked then you'll just love' section, and you can check out the stars' birthdays. Another good database site is **www.allmovie.com**, which has a really good search engine.

www.filmworld.co.uk
THE ONE STOP FILM SHOP

ʊ ʊ ʊ ʊ ʊ

COUNTRY UK

A brilliant film buff's site. What really makes this site stand out is its very good search facility and the way it combines a great review site with an excellent shop. The shop offers film memorabilia, finds out of print movies, and offers up to

25% off current ones. Delivery is £1. It also has trailers, competitions and lots of information.

www.aintcoolnews.com
AIN'T IT JUST COOL

☺☺☺☺☺
COUNTRY USA

A renowned review site that can make or break a movie in the US, it's very entertaining and likeable. Harry Knowles' movie reviews are by far the best bit of the site. You can search the archive for a particular review or contribute a bit of juicy gossip by e-mailing Harry direct. See also **www.moviecritic.com** where you can also rate movies yourself, but you have to become a member.

www.oneworldlive.com
YOUR BACKSTAGE PASS TO HOLLYWOOD GOSSIP

☺☺☺
COUNTRY USA

The latest gossip, news and views from Hollywood; it's easier to use than most as it works like a good celebrity magazine. Also check out **www.hollywood.com**, which has over 1 million pages of information and trailers.

www.warnervillage.co.uk.
BOOK YOUR TICKETS ON-LINE

☺☺☺
COUNTRY UK

Warner's is a really good film site. You can buy films, see trailers and reviews, plus you can buy cinema tickets on-line. Odeon promise a similar web site soon; huge on-line demand for ticket bookings forced them to redesign their site.

www.popcorn.co.uk
FROM POSTERS TO WHAT'S ON

☺☺☺☺☺ Almost the complete package from Carlton TV,

COUNTRY UK — a great site for movie buffs as well as reliable local cinema listings complete with trailers giving you a taster before put your coat on.

www.moviesounds.com
LISTEN TO YOUR FAVOURITE MOVIES

☺☺☺ Download extracts from over 50 movies, it's a

COUNTRY USA — little confusing at first but once you've got the technology sorted out it's good fun.

http://rinkworks.com/movieaminute/
DON'T HAVE TIME TO WATCH IT ALL?

☺☺☺☺☺ Summaries of the top movies for those who

COUNTRY USA — either can't be bothered to watch them or just want to pretend they did, either way it's really funny. For a list of all the clichés that happen in movies check out **www.moviecliches.com**.

Film companies

Some of the best web sites are those that promote a particular film, here is a list of the major film producers and their web sites, which are all good and have links to the latest releases. Most have clips, downloads, screensavers and lots of advertising.

www.disney.com
www.foxmovies.com
www.mca.com
www.miramax.com
www.paramount.com
www.spe.sony.com
www.foxmovies.com
www.uip.com
www.universalpictures.com
www.warnerbros.com

Buying movies

It's probably best to start with visiting a price
checker site first such as **www.kelkoo.com**
(see page 149) but these are the best of the
movie on-line stores.

www.blackstar.co.uk
THE UK'S BIGGEST VIDEO STORE

☺☺☺☺ The biggest on-line video and DVD retailer, it
COUNTRY UK claims to be able to get around 50,000 titles.
Blackstar is very good value, boasts free delivery
and has a reputation for excellent customer
service.

If shopping around try **www.blockbuster.com**,
who have different offers.

www.dvdstreet.infront.co.uk
FOR DVD ONLY

☺☺☺☺☺
COUNTRY UK

Part of the Streetsonline group, this is a great value and easy-to-use site that only sells DVD. But there's lots of other movie-related features too such as the latest news, gossip and reviews. Delivery is free for the UK.

www.movietrak.com
RENT A DVD MOVIE

☺☺☺☺
COUNTRY UK

The latest films are available to rent for £2.99 for 9 days. Pick the title of your choice and it's dispatched the same day, you then return it 7 days later in the pre-paid envelope. The range offered is excellent covering ten major categories plus the latest releases, coming soon and a good search facility too.

www.reel.com
OVER 100,000 MOVIES

☺☺☺☺
COUNTRY USA

Here is a mixture of news, gossip, interviews, event listings and US-style outright selling. The content is really good and you can get carried away browsing. The search facility is very good but shipping to the UK costs a minimum of $6. Watch out for local taxes and ensure that you can actually play the video in the UK. Also sells DVD and CDs.

Music and radio

Before spending your hard earned cash on CDs check out
MP3. MP3 technology allows the compression of a music
track into a file, which can be stored and played back.

An MP3 player can be downloaded free on to your PC
from several sites, the best being the original at
www.mp3.com or the popular **www.real.com** *and its*
RealPlayer. It takes minutes to download the player and if
you play CDs on your PC it will also record them.

You'll then be able to listen to samples available at
music stores. Once you've joined the MP3 revolution,
there's an amazing amount of free music available. Start at
either web site where there are excellent search facilities.
Other good MP3 players include **www.sonique.com** *which*
is the best looking, although you can do more with
Winamp at **www.winamp.com**. *You can also try*
www.liquidaudio.com.

Other sites with lots of MP3 downloads that are worth
checking out are listed below. If you're in a band you can
apply to have your music available to download on some
of the sites.

www.getoutthere.bt.com is particularly good
www.audiofind.com brilliant search engine

www.songs.com good for American artists

www.soundresource.net great for sound effects – some rude!

www.emusic.com over 6700 artists, great but you have to pay

www.listen.com good for a wide variety of music, fiddly to use

www.napster.com

THE NAPSTER MUSIC COMMUNITY

☺☺☺☺ Once you've downloaded the Napster program, you can locate and download your favourite music in MP3 format from one convenient, easy-to-use web site. This means that you can literally share the downloaded music of thousands of other MP3 fans. You could also check out the more complicated world of Gnutella (http://gnutella.wego.com), which sounds like something you spread on toast, but is a very sophisticated way of sharing data and music.

COUNTRY USA

Check with whoever pays the bills before downloading anything, though the sites listed are probably safe, there's always the chance of the download being infected with a virus. If in doubt save to a disk first. Some files take a long time to download so watch the phone bill.

Buying music

If you've been let loose with a credit card, it's as well to start by checking prices of CDs through price comparison sites such as those listed in our main shopping section. These will take you to the store offering the best combination of price and postage. All the stores listed below offer good value plus a bit extra.

www.jungle.com
JUNGLE MANIA!

☺☺☺☺   Jungle is easy, great fun to use and good value.
COUNTRY   UK   In the Jungle Beat section you get all the latest in music and a massive back catalogue. There's good information even on obscure albums. They also have great offers on DVDs and videos, masses of games for PCs and other formats, plus a wide selection of computers, software, hardware and consumables (disks, ink cartridges etc). There is a loyalty scheme and delivery is free. Jungle also offers e-mail and an order tracking service.

www.hmv.com.uk
HIS MASTER'S VOICE ON-LINE

☺☺☺☺   Excellent features and offers on the latest CDs
COUNTRY   UK   and videos. There are sections on most aspects of music as well as video, DVD and games with

a good search facility. You can listen to selections from albums before buying providing that you have RealPlayer. Spoken word or books on tape are available as well.

www.virginmega.com
THE VIRGIN MEGASTORE

☺☺☺☺
COUNTRY UK

Loads of music categories means that you are spoilt for choice and you get good prices and free delivery. There is the usual search facility and loads of recommendations to help you. Become a Virgin V.I.P. and get special offers selected just for you. An interesting feature is the Virgin free radio. Unfortunately the site is a little slow.

www.cdnow.com
NOT JUST CDs

☺☺☺☺
COUNTRY USA

One of the original and easiest to use of the music sites, it has lots of features, such as downloads (which enable you to sample albums for 30 days), a video section and a recommendation service. Unfortunately, UK residents can't take advantage of the excellent custom CD service.

www.cduniverse.com
FOR THE WIDEST RANGE AND GREAT OFFERS

☺☺☺☺
COUNTRY USA

Probably the site with the very best offers. There is a massive range to choose from and delivery normally takes only 5 days. You can also buy games, DVD and video. Excellent, but can be quite slow.

For more great offers on CDs try: **www.cdparadise.co.uk**.

www.101cd.com
1.6 MILLION TITLES
☺☺☺☺
COUNTRY UK

A massive selection to choose from, plus great prices make 101cd as good as most music stores. It also offers really good customer service and it's the only store we've found with a browsable listing of available mini-discs.

Bands, groups and stars

www.ubl.com
THE ULTIMATE BAND LIST
☺☺☺☺
COUNTRY USA

It is the place for mountains of information on groups or singers. It has a totally brilliant search facility and you can buy from the site as well. Prices are not as good as elsewhere.

For a similar, but better organised site, try **www.allmusic.com**, where you can also get excellent information and videos.

www.eartothesound.fsnet.co.uk/home.html

REVIEWS

☺ ☺ ☺ ☺
COUNTRY UK

They call themselves the ultimate review site and it's really great, except that they concentrate almost entirely on rock music. If that's your poison, then it's perfect.

Where to find the bands and stars:
A1 www.a1-online.com
Aaliyah www.aaliyahonline.com
Abba www.abbasite.com
Christina Aguilera www.christina-a.com
Christina Aguilera www.christina-aguilera.com
All Saints http://allsaints.ukmix.net
Shola Ama www.shola-ama.com
Vanessa Amorosi www.vanessaamorosi.com
Atomic Kitten www.atomickitten.com
Backstreet Boys
   www.backstreetboys.com
Mel B www.melanieb.net
BBMak www.bbmak.co.uk
Victoria Beckham http://poshpalace.cjb.net
Blur www.blur.co.uk
Britney Spears www.britneyspears.com
B'witched www.b-witched.com
Boyzone www.boyzone.co.uk
Emma Bunton www.emma-bunton.de
Mariah Carey www.mcarey.com
Mariah Carey www.imcorg.com

Mel C www.melcnews.com
Craig David www.craigdavid.co.uk
Coldplay www.coldplay.com
Eminem www.eminem.com
Fierce www.fierce.co.k
Five www.5ive.com
Girl Thing www.click2music.co.uk/girlthing/
David Gray www.davidgray.com
Macy Gray www.macygray.com
Geri Halliwell www.gerihalliwell.com
Whitney Houston www.whitney-houston.com
Natalie Imbruglia www.natalie-imbruglia.co.uk
Janet Jackson http://missjanet.xs4all.nl/
Janet Jackson www.janet-jackson.com
Michael Jackson www.mjifc.com
Ronan Keating www.ronankeating.net
Madonna www.wbr.com/madonna
Manic Street Preachers www.manics.co.uk
Ricky Martin www.rickymartin.com
Moby www.moby.org
Samantha Mumba www.samanthamumba.com
Northern Line www.northern-line.com
N Sync www.nsync.com
Pink www.spingolo.com/pink
Billie Piper http://c3.vmg.co.uk/billie/
Point Break www.point-break.net
Scooch www.scooch.com
Sclub7 www.sclub7.co.uk
Sclub7 www.sclub.com

Sisqo www.sisqo.com

Sister2Sister www.s2s.com.au/

Will Smith www.willsmith.com

Sonique www.sonique.co.uk

Spice Girls
   http://c3.vmg.co.uk/spicegirls/nowspice/

Spice Girls
   www.virginrecords.com/spice_girls/spice.html

Steps www.stepsofficial.com

Steps www.welcome.to/steps_the_web_site/

Texas
   www.geocities.com/zerotexaszero/home.html

Travis www.travisonline.com

Vengaboys www.vengaboys.com

Westlife www.westlife.co.uk

Robbie Williams www.hestheone.co.uk

Robbie Williams www.theegohaslanded.co.uk

Music, TV and magazine sites

www.bbc.co.uk/totp/ or www.totp.beeb.com

TOP OF THE POPS

☺☺☺☺

COUNTRY UK

Both the Top of the Pops sites are different, the site at **bbc.co.uk** is more like a magazine, the one at **beeb.com** is more like a shop. That said, there are loads of good features and articles as well as competitions, trivia and info by the ton in both of them, so maybe it doesn't matter which one you go to.

www.mtv.co.uk
MUSIC TELEVISION

☺☺☺☺

COUNTRY UK

MTV offers loads of info on events, shows and the artists as well as stuff on the presenters. There are also creative bits like movie and music video clips. Great design.

www.music365.com
MUSIC NEWS

☺☺☺☺☺

COUNTRY UK

Fantastic for all the latest goss and news from the pop world, hot stories, charts, competitions, reviews and you can even sample some of the latest releases too. A good alternative is www.pop-music.net which is really well-designed but has less stuff.

www.music-mag.com
NEWS AND REVIEWS

☺☺☺

COUNTRY UK

A good, cool-looking, all-round music site covering all aspects of modern music in a straightforward style. It has a really good section on clubbing, but at the time of writing some sections such as the lifestyle and links were still in development. If they get as good as the rest, this will be a 5-star site soon.

www.nme.com
NEW MUSICAL EXPRESS

☺ ☺ ☺

COUNTRY UK

Ah the oldies are the best...it's not up to the standards of 365 but if you're a rock fan, then this is where it's at. There's all the usual information, but the graphics sometimes don't line up and the 'angst' section is a waste of space.

www.qonline.co.uk
Q MAGAZINE

☺ ☺ ☺ ☺

COUNTRY UK

A very adult music magazine with over 18,000 reviews, plus features and articles that cover most aspects of music. It doesn't miss much.

www.popworld.com
WHERE POP COMES FIRST

☺ ☺ ☺ ☺ ☺

COUNTRY UK

A brilliant new site that concentrates on pop, it's fun and has great graphics. You have to register to join but once you're in you get access to competitions, features on your favourite bands, clips from Popworld TV, fashion tips and much more. Coooelll.

www.thebox.co.uk
SMASH HITS YOU CONTROL

☺ ☺ ☺ ☺

COUNTRY UK

Similar to 365 and Q but with added features such as the ability for you to select a tune to be played on their TV channel and you can influence their overall selection by voting for your favourite songs.

Specific musical sites

www.darkerthanblue.com/
HOME OF BLACK MUSIC

☺☺☺☺

COUNTRY UK

Very well-designed site dedicated to black-influenced music and musicians, it has all the latest news, gig guides, artist features and downloads.

www.bluesworld.com
HOMAGE TO THE BLUES

☺☺☺☺

COUNTRY USA

If you're into the blues then this is your kind of site. There are interviews, memorabilia, 78's auctions, bibliographies, discographies and lists of links to other blues sites. You can order CDs and if the mood takes you, order a guitar too.

www.classicalmusic.co.uk
ALL YOU NEED TO KNOW ABOUT CLASSICAL MUSIC

☺☺☺

COUNTRY UK

Excellent for lovers of classical music with articles, guides, reviews and concert listings. You can also buy CDs from the Global Music Network who aren't the cheapest, so it may pay to buy elsewhere. For another very informative site with an excellent selection of links try **www.classical.net** or for offers **www.mdcmusic.co.uk**.

www.anthems.com
DANCE, HOUSE AND GARAGE

ごごごごご
COUNTRY UK

Great design combined with brilliant content, there's everything here for dance fans – news, info on raves and samples of the latest mixes. If you're feeling rich you can buy from the site, although you'll probably find cheaper elsewhere.

For an alternative view of the dance scene try www.fly.co.uk, who have a real urban look to their site. For links to over 500 dance-related sites and a complete listing of new releases go to www.juno.co.uk.

www.puresilk.co.uk
ENTER THE REALM

ごごご
COUNTRY UK

Really flash site with loads of great graphics and as they say – pizzazz. Find out what the pioneers of UK garage are up to and all the details of their activities in Ibiza and Ayia Napa.

www.thedsc.com/
HIP, HOP AND RAP

ごごごご
COUNTRY UK

Da saga continues… news, reviews and features on Hip Hop, there's a good selection of links to other related sites and if you're a real fan you can voice your opinions by becoming a writer for them. For a really good alternative check out www.peeps.com.

www.playlouder.com
INDIE MUSIC

☺☺☺☺

COUNTRY USA

Great graphics and excellent design make Playlouder stand out from the crowd. It covers the Indie music scene in depth with all the usual features, but with a bit more style. Another really well-designed web site covering Indie music in great detail is Channel Fly **www.channelfly.com** – take your pick!

www.jazzonln.com
JAZZ ON-LINE

☺☺☺☺☺

COUNTRY USA

Whether you need help in working your way through the minefield that is jazz music, or you know what you want, Jazz On-line can provide it. Its easy format covers all styles and it has a brill search facility. There is a good chat section and you can ask Jazz Messenger just about anything. You can't buy from the site but there are links to Amazon's music section. Try also **www.jazze.com** and **www.jazzcorner.com**.

www.operadata.co.uk
OPERA NOW MAGAZINE

☺☺☺

COUNTRY UK

This site gives opera listings and provides background to the history of opera. To get the most out of it you have to subscribe to **Opera Now** magazine. For the **Opera Magazine** site go to **www.opera.co.uk**

www.rbpage.com
R&B AND SOUL
☺☺☺☺

COUNTRY USA

The R&B page is the place to go if you've got soul, and you've got it bad. You can sample the latest releases, catch up on the R&B news, read reviews or artist biogs and there's a great set of links too.

www.reggaesource.com
REGGAE
☺☺☺☺☺

COUNTRY USA

Great looking site with lots of info on the artists, albums, events, clubs and where in the world you can listen to reggae. There are also reviews and links to other reggae related sites.

Music information

www.clickmusic.co.uk
EVERYTHING YOU NEED TO KNOW ABOUT MUSIC
☺☺☺☺

COUNTRY UK

This is great for all music fans. It has quick access to details on any particular band, plus tickets, downloads, gigs and gossip. Shopping is straightforward using their Best 10 listings, just click on the store or use the search engine to find something specific.

www.dotmusic.com
ALL THE MUSIC NEWS

☻☻☻☻☻
COUNTRY UK
Get the latest 'insider' views from the music industry with reviews, charts, chat and a good value on-line shop. These combined with the fab design make this a totally excellent site. You can access this site from some WAP phones.

www.musicsearch.com
THE INTERNET'S MUSIC SEARCH ENGINE

☻☻☻☻
COUNTRY USA
Not that easy-to-use, but keep at it, if you need to find that track or artist, or need information on a particular instrument or commercial aspect of music. You can search the on-line stores for good deals or where to get the best range.

www.lyrics.com
THE WORDS TO HUNDREDS OF SONGS

☻☻☻☻
COUNTRY USA
There are songs from over 100 bands and artists including Oasis, Madonna, Britney Spears and even Queen. You can also make requests and see if you know the words to any of the songs in the most wanted section. Don't expect to find any old favourites or classics though. For an alternative see **www.songfile.com,** which also offers a good selection of songs.

www.kissthisguy.com

MISHEARD LYRICS

☺ ☺ ☺ ☺　Mr Misheard lists all those lyrics that you

COUNTRY USA　thought were being sung but in reality you were just not quite listening properly. We liked 'I am the Firestarter' misheard as 'I am a big fat hamster' but there are hundreds more.

Concerts and tickets

www.liveconcerts.com

WELCOME TO THE CYBERCAST

☺ ☺ ☺　Watch live concerts on-line! A great idea but let

COUNTRY USA　down by 'net congestion'. You need RealPlayer to see the concerts and listen to the interviews and recordings. It's very good for sampling different types of music and you can buy CDs as well.

www.bigmouth.co.uk

UK'S MOST COMPREHENSIVE GIG GUIDE

☺ ☺ ☺　UK based, with lots of links to band sites,

COUNTRY UK　news, events listing and information on what's up and coming. A great search facility and the ability to buy tickets make this a really useful site for gig lovers everywhere. It's geared to rock and pop. For tour dates in the USA try **www.tourdates.com**.

www.ticketmaster.co.uk
TICKETS FOR EVERYTHING

☺☺☺☺ Book tickets for just about anything and you can
COUNTRY UK run searches by venue, city or date. The site is
split into four key sections:

1. All Arts – theatre, classical, dance, comedy
   and events
2. All Concerts – gigs, jazz, clubs, rock and pop.
3. All Family – shows, anything from Disney on
   Ice to air shows.
4. All Sports – tickets for virtually every
   sporting occasion.

www.concertphoto.co.uk
PHOTOS OF YOUR FAVOURITE BANDS

☺☺☺☺ OK so you've been to the gig and you didn't take
COUNTRY UK a camera, well the chances are that Pete Still has
a photo available for you to buy from this great
web site. There are hundred of bands to choose
from, both old and new, and he's covered the
major festivals too. Costs vary according to size
and quantity.

Aspiring artists

www.taxi.com
FOR UNSIGNED BANDS

☺☺☺☺ Looking to get a music contract for your
COUNTRY USA band? You should start here, there's loads of

information, contacts and links that will help
you on the rocky road to success and stardom.
Well, that's the theory anyway.

www.irz.com/robin/bandnameprogam
GENERATOR OF RANDOM BAND NAMES

☺☺☺   So you can't think of a name for your band?
COUNTRY USA   Well help is at hand, just pull the GORBY lever
and your new band name will appear. At
www.joescafe.com/bands there is the Band-o-
matic which will offer all sorts of never-before-
used band names in seconds.

Radio

You need a decent downloadable player such as
RealPlayer (see introduction) or Windows Media
Player before you start listening. RealPlayer in
particular gives you access to loads of stations
and allows you to add more. The downside
is that quality is sometimes affected by 'net
congestion'.

www.bbc.co.uk/radio
THE BEST OF THE BBC

☺☺☺☺☺   Listen to the news and the latest hits while you
COUNTRY UK   do your homework, just select the station you
want. There's also loads of information on each
major station, as well as a comprehensive listing

service. Some features will be missing due to rights issues. The Radio 1 pages have details on all the DJs, samples, news, interviews, live web cams, and you can sometimes e-mail them as well as get all the gossip and info.

www.virginradio.com

VIRGIN ON AIR

☺ ☺ ☺ ☺ ☺ Excellent web site with plenty of stuff about the
COUNTRY UK station, its schedule and stars. There's also the latest music news. The site has an annoying amount of advertising though. You can listen if you have Quicktime, Windows Media Player or RealPlayer.

Other independent radio stations on-line are:
www.classicfm.com – using Windows Media Player
www.jazzfm.com – using Windows Media Player
www.galaxy-radio.co.uk – using Windows Media Player
www.capitalfm.com – Capital Radio using RealPlayer
www.coolfm.co.uk – using RealPlayer
www.heart1062.co.uk – using Windows Media Player
www.lbc.co.uk – using Real Audio.

www.radioacademy.org
UK'S GATEWAY TO RADIO

☺☺☺☺☺

COUNTRY UK

Radio Academy is a charity that covers all things to do with radio including news, events and its advancement in education and information. It has a list of all UK stations including those that offer web casts. For another massive list of stations go to Yahoo's **www.broadcast.com/radio**.

www.netradio.net
RADIO TAILORED JUST FOR YOU

☺☺☺☺

COUNTRY USA

Pick any one of its specialist 120 channels; tune in using RealPlayer or Windows Media Player, and if you like the track you can also buy the album. A specialist has programmed each channel to play a type of music and the selection is consistently good, this site has a real 'wow' factor. Other good radio sites are **www.comfm.fr** a French site with access to almost 3,500 live stations and the American **www.webradio.com**.

News and weather

www.sky.co.uk/news

THE ULTIMATE NEWS SITE

☺☺☺☺☺

COUNTRY UK

Sky News has a reputation for excellence and that is reflected in their web site. It's got the best all round news service with good coverage across the world as well as the UK. You can view news clips, listen to news items or just browse the site. There are also sections on sport, business, technology and even a few games.

Other great sites for news are:
www.bbc.co.uk/news – the BBC site is great for regional news as well as UK and the world
www.itn.co.uk – supplies all the news to ITV
www.teletext.co.uk – nothing like what you see on the telly, this is excellent
www.cnn.com – world news
www.abcnews.com – the American view.

www.met-office.gov.uk

EXCELLING IN WEATHER SERVICES

☺☺☺☺☺

COUNTRY UK

Everything you need to know about Britain's favourite topic of conversation. Get forecasts by region, city or for the whole country complete with pressure charts, satellite images and the usual charts. There is international forecasting too. You'll find great background information to the weather and a good selection of weather-related links.

www.bbc.co.uk/weather
ANOTHER WINNER FROM THE BBC

☺☺☺☺☺
COUNTRY UK

The BBC site gives up to the minute and five-day forecasts, ski reports, sun index, world weather and the shipping forecast. It is very clear and concise and backed up with weather-related articles.

For more information, the Weather Channel has a very good site on **www.weather.com**. This is geared to the USA, but has some really good articles and features.

www.weatherimages.org
SEE THE WORLD'S WEATHER – LIVE

☺☺☺☺
COUNTRY UK

The Weatherimages site is put together by true weather fans and has masses of information, but bear in mind it's an amateur site. The best bit is the Weather Cams, from which you can see the world's weather from the Antartic to Northern Europe via Bondi beach or Rio. It's spoiled a little by intrusive advertising though.

On-line magazines

On-line magazines or e-zines as they are sometimes called, offer all the features of a conventional magazine except that there's much more space available. As a result, they can cover stuff in more depth, run more competitions and give you the chance to get more involved in what interests you. There are hundreds, but here are some of the best listed in alphabetical order. There's a guide to the target age of readership too.

General mags

www.4degreez.com
INTERACTIVE COMMUNITY

☺ ☺ ☺
COUNTRY USA
AGE 15 PLUS

A friendly and entertaining site with reviews, poetry, jokes, polls and links to other related sites, you have to become a member to get the best out of it though.

www.aboutteens.org
ABOUT TEENS

☺ ☺ ☺
COUNTRY USA
AGE 13 PLUS

You won't learn much about teens here, but there are some good jokes, stories and funny photos.

www.alloy.com
ALLOY ANNOY

☻☻☻

COUNTRY USA

AGE 13 PLUS

On the face of it this is great, it's got loads of sections on everything from personal advice to shopping. But it's spoiled by too many adverts and every time you click on a new section another load of boxes pop up with yet more adverts. Could it be geared to getting your name for marketing purposes?

www.bamboozled.org
FIND TRUTH IN YOUTH

☻☻☻

COUNTRY USA

AGE 13 PLUS

A good looking and serious site featuring articles, poems and stories from young people in San Francisco.

www.bbc.co.uk/so
So

☻☻☻☻

COUNTRY UK

AGE 10 PLUS

The BBC have done a great job with the colourful *So* mag, it's got really excellent stuff such as quizzes, music, problems, interviews, fashion, weird, links and a chat section. There's also some brilliant competitions and prizes.

www.brit-teen.com
FOR BRITISH TEENAGERS

☻☻☻

COUNTRY UK

AGE 13 PLUS

Entertaining, with a mixture of news, views, TV and music Brit-teen tries really hard to please. There's also a problem clinic, chat room and links to other interesting web sites. It can be a little out-of-date sometimes.

www.cheekfreak.com
FOR THE FREAK IN ALL OF US

☺ ☺ ☺ ☺

COUNTRY USA

AGE 13 PLUS

Best for stories, on-line diaries and free downloads. It's got chat sections, message boards and a search engine. They deserve a medal for the pranks section which is brilliant (not something parents would approve of).

www.crankymag.com
CRANKY

☺ ☺ ☺

COUNTRY USA

AGE 15 PLUS

There are some fun and useful things here, articles, features and poems, but some of the links don't work and it doesn't seem to get updated that often.

www.cyberteens.com
CONNECT TO CYBERTEENS

☺ ☺ ☺

COUNTRY USA

AGE 13 PLUS

One of the most hyped sites aimed at teenagers, it contains a good selection of games, news, links and a creativity section where you can send your art and poems. Don't bother with the shop, it's expensive, as is the credit card they offer.

www.globalgang.org.uk
WORLD NEWS, GAMES, GOSSIP AND FUN

☺ ☺ ☺

COUNTRY UK

AGE 10 PLUS

See what the rest of the world gets up to at Global Gang. You can find out what kids in other countries like to eat, what toys they play with, chat to them or play games. Lastly, you get to find out how you can help kids less fortunate than yourself.

www.kidsonline.co.uk

BLUE JAM

☺ ☺ ☺ ☺ ☺
COUNTRY UK
AGE 10 PLUS

Blue Jam is excellent; it has everything – WAP, pets, news, plus games, reviews, event listings, links and competitions. There's also a good advice section. There's also a version for younger kids too.

www.onthecurb.org

WRITTEN BY YOUNG PEOPLE FOR YOUNG PEOPLE

☺ ☺ ☺
COUNTRY USA
AGE 13 PLUS

A streetwise e-zine aimed at teenagers who are 'busy making the world a better place'. There's some interesting stuff here, and it does give a good view of what it's like being a teenager in the USA.

www.teentoday.co.uk

FOR TEENAGERS BY TEENAGERS

☺ ☺ ☺ ☺
COUNTRY USA
AGE 13 PLUS

Get your free e-zine mailed to you daily or just visit the site which has much more: games, chat, news, entertainment, free downloads and message boards. It's well-designed and genuinely good with not too much advertising.

www.thinkdiff.com
DIFFERENT
☺ ☺ ☺ ☺   Thinkdiff is a site that has everything from
COUNTRY INDIA   sport, news, crosswords, and stories, even cook-
AGE 13 PLUS   ery. It really is different to the usual sites aimed
at young people.

www.urban75.co.uk
WITH ATTITUDE
☺ ☺ ☺ ☺   Advert free and punchy, this e-zine has got
COUNTRY UK   information on how to be an eco-warrior, sports
AGE 16 PLUS   news, photography and some really useless
games. It tells you how to put on your own rave
party and where the best ones are, and best of all
you get to 'punch' your least favourite celebrity.
There is some strong language here.

Mags for girls

There seems to be hundreds of web sites aimed
at teenage girls, here are the best of them.

www.agirlsworld.com
WHERE GIRLS RULE THE WEB
☺ ☺ ☺   Regular columns and features, plus problem
COUNTRY USA   pages, surveys, competitions, entertainment
AGE 11 PLUS   news and special clubs mean that there's more
here than found on most similar sites. It's
geared to American girls though. Check out

www.americangirl.com too, this has more in the
way of things to do.

www.chickclick.com
FOR THE INDEPENDENT GIRL

☺☺☺☺

COUNTRY USA

AGE 15 PLUS

A year ago this site was aimed at much younger
girls but now what more could you want?
Information on every key thing in life, what's
cool, what's not and who's in who's not. You
can set it up as your home page, with your own
chickclick.com e-mail address and enter into the
spirit of sisterhood by visiting the chat rooms.
There are links to sister sites too, which may be
more adult in content. For other sites with a bit
of attitude check out **www.riotgrrl.com** which is
good on celebrity stuff or **www.foxymag.com**,
who have minimal style but good articles, information and an excellent links section.

www.cybergrrlz.com
ON-LINE COMMUNITY FOR GIRLS (AND SMARTER GUYS)

☺☺☺☺

COUNTRY USA

AGE 11 PLUS

With good advice, humour, quizzes, opinions,
reviews and links to other related sites
Cybergrrlz has lots to offer. It's friendly and
easy-to-use and it's updated regularly so the
features are spot on.

www.girltech.com
FOR THE ADVENTUROUS SPIRIT

☺☺☺☺

COUNTRY USA

AGE 11 PLUS

This site has several main sections; Chick Chat is self explanatory, Girl Galaxy looks at what women have achieved through history, InventHer at what they've invented, Girl Views is about girls in the news, play games at Game Café or browse related links in the Tech Trip. It's all very positive and designed to encourage you to achieve. For a less techy but similar site go to Girl Power **www.health.org/gpower** which is similar in tone, but there's more emphasis on advice and health.

www.mykindaplace.com
YOUR KINDA SITE

☺☺☺

COUNTRY UK

A British site that is close in style to a proper magazine with sections on showbiz, TV, beauty and fashion, plus good advice and chat. There's lots of advertising and emphasis on retail therapy – shopping.

www.wowgo.com
A WAY OF LIFE

☺☺☺☺

COUNTRY UK

To borrow a quote from them 'No brothers, no parents, no boys, no teachers, and no web weirdos waiting to pounce! Wowgo is a 100% girl thing where you don't have to just love it, you can live it!' There's much more variety and content than the average magazine, possibly the best we visited. It's also very well designed and good-looking too.

Real mags on-line

The publishers of *Sugar* and *TV Hits* are planning to launch a web site soon, using material from both mags, so watch out for that.

At the time of writing *Jump*'s web site was under construction but looks really promising, it's at **www.jumponline.com**.

There are no sites for *Bliss*, *Smash Hits*, *MG*, *Shout*, *Looks*, *J17*, *Fresh*, *19* or *Mizz*.

The Beeb have a page for *Live and Kicking* magazine at **www.bbc.co.uk/kicking/magazine.shtml**. However, it's geared to getting you to buy the mag, there's a few games, quizzes and competitions though.

Comics

www.kingfeatures.com
AMERICAN COMICS

☺ ☺ ☺ ☺
COUNTRY USA
AGE 5 TO 15

Cartoon strips from many favourites; Popeye, Denis the Menace, Hagar and the Phantom to name a few, plus some you've maybe never heard of. It's worth a look just for Zippy the Pinhead.

www.beano.co.uk
BEANO – YOU KNOW YOU LOVE IT

☺ ☺ ☺

COUNTRY UK

AGE 5 PLUS

Play games, meet the characters and get yourself involved with what goes on in Beanotown. It's good, but slow and some younger kids will need some help with using it.

Pets

Here are some great web sites that you can use to help you look after or choose a pet.

www.pets-pyjamas.co.uk
THE COMPLETE PET'S WEB SITE

☺ ☺ ☺ ☺

COUNTRY UK

Go to Petmags for news and information, take part in on-line discussions, chat in Petpals, do a competition or quiz in Petfun, even set up a web site for your pet. The most important section is Petshops consisting of Pets Pyjama's own shop plus links to a bookshop with over 1000 titles and **www.animail.co.uk** a more general, but good value pet shop. For another good on-line pet store visit **www.petplanet.co.uk** or **www.petlink.co.uk** who have an excellent set of links to other pet sites.

www.petmad.com
PET MAD!

☺ ☺ ☺ ☺

COUNTRY UK

Great on-line pet shop that is particularly good at catering for the needs of small pets, with lots of advice, tips and how to choose one.

www.birdcare.co.uk
CARING FOR YOUR BIRD

☺ ☺ ☺
COUNTRY UK

Everything you need to know about looking after pet birds, with links to specialist sites and a free ask the vet service.

www.dogsonline.co.uk
DOGS, DOGS AND MORE DOGS

☺ ☺ ☺ ☺
COUNTRY UK

Everything you could ever want from a web site about dogs. There's information on breeding, where to get dogs, events, directories, how to find hotels that accept dogs, classified ads and insurance.

For more information on dogs try **www.canismajor.com** an American magazine site, or **www.canineworld.com**. The official line on dogs and breeding, with information on Crufts and links to more doggy web sites is found at **www.the-kennel-club.org.uk**.

www.ncdl.org.uk
NATIONAL CANINE DEFENCE LEAGUE

☺ ☺ ☺
COUNTRY UK

Excellent web site featuring the works of the NCDL, the largest charity of its type. Get advice on how to adopt a dog, tips on looking after one and download a doggy screensaver. For Battersea Dogs Home go to **www.dogshome.org** who also have a well-designed site.

www.cats.org.uk
HOME OF CAT PROTECTION

☺☺☺☺
COUNTRY UK

Nice site, with information on caring, re-homing, news and general advice. For young children there's a section called the Kitten club and an archive of cat photos. There's also an on-line shop that offers free delivery in the UK. For even more information on cats go to **www.moggies.co.uk**. Not an easy site to use, but has a really excellent set of links to other pet sites.

www.equiworld.net
GLOBAL EQUINE INFORMATION

☺☺☺☺☺
COUNTRY UK

A directory, magazine and advice centre in one, with incredible detail on horses, plus some fun stuff too. The shop is basically a set of links to specialist traders though. For horsy health advice go to **www.horseadvice.com**, which has loads of information. Check out the mega **www.equine-world.co.uk** too.

www.pethealthcare.co.uk
PET INSURANCE

☺☺☺
COUNTRY UK

If you're looking for insurance to cover the vet's bill, then here's a good place to start. For other comparable quotes try **www.healty-pets.co.uk**.

www.giveusahome.co.uk
RE-HOMING A PET

☺ ☺ ☺ ☺   A nice idea – a web site devoted to helping you
COUNTRY UK   save animals that need to be re-homed. It's got a
                 large amount of information by region on shel-
                 ters, vets and the animals themselves as well as
                 entertaining cartoons.

www.rspca.org.uk
OFFICIAL RSPCA SITE

☺ ☺ ☺ ☺ ☺   Nice looking site, with a big 'ahh' factor that has
COUNTRY UK   lots of information on the work of the RSPCA.
                 includes how you can help and advice on how to
                 look after animals, and what to do if you know
                 of any that need help.

Phones and phone numbers

In this section there's information on where to go to buy mobiles, get the best out of them and even have a little fun with them. There's also advice on finding someone's number.

www.buy.co.uk/personal/calculators/mobiles.asp
MOBILE PHONE CALCULATOR

ⴣ ⴣ ⴣ ⴣ   Get the right tariff and save money. It's easy-to-
COUNTRY UK use and you can do it all on-line.

www.carphonewarehouse.com
CHOOSING THE RIGHT MOBILE

ⴣ ⴣ ⴣ ⴣ ⴣ You need to take your time to find the best tariff
COUNTRY UK using their calculator, then take advantage of the
numerous offers. Excellent pictures and details
of all phones while all the info is unbiased.
Delivery is free too.

    Another good site is **www.miahtelecom.co.uk**
who, apart from good offers, have an easy-to-
use tariff calculator.

www.genie.co.uk
WAP PHONES MADE USEFUL

ⴣ ⴣ ⴣ   Loads of information on what you can do if
COUNTRY UK you've got a WAP phone, but it's a really boring

site, so you have to be patient and hunt for the good stuff.

Here's where to find the major phone operators:

www.orange.co.uk

www.vodafone.co.uk (www.vizzavi.co.uk for their WAP service)

www.one2one.co.uk

www.cellnet.co.uk

www.bt.co.uk

www.virginmobile.com

www.yourmobile.com

NEW RING TONES FOR YOUR PHONE

☺ ☺ ☺ ☺

COUNTRY UK

There are over 100 tunes that you can download on to your mobile using text messaging. At the time of writing it only works on Nokia phones, but it's bound to catch on.

Text messaging

An emoticon is a fancy name for those helpful little abbreviations we all use in text messages, the smiley being the original. You can find as many as you'll ever need at www.chatlist.com/faces.html but hey, whatever, here's our small selection anyway.

Angry >:-(	*Laugh* :-D
Angry :-@	*Oops* :-*
Blabber mouth (:-D	*Pig* :8)
Blow a kiss :-x	*No comment* ( )
Cry :'-(	Not amused %-{
Crying :'-(	*Sad* :-(
Embarrassed :-}	*Sarcasm* :->
Flirt @;-)	*Secret* :-X
Great party #-)	*Shock* :-O
Great! I like it! :^D	*Shout* : ( )
Hangover #-(	*Swear to secrecy* :X
Happy :-)	*Talk* :-v
Hug []	*Tired/Yawn* >-0
Hugs & Kisses {{**}}	

Along with the emoticons go text message acronyms:

ASAP *As soon as possible*
BFN *Bye for now*
CUL8R *See you later*
F2F *Face to face (also meeting in person)*
FAQ *Frequently asked questions*
HHOJ *Ha ha only joking*
NRN *No reply necessary*

OIC   *Oh I see*
rehi   *Hello again*
TNX   *Thanks*
TTFN   *Ta-ta for now*
TTYL   *Talk to you later*

Phone numbers

Lost a phone number, need to get in touch or just find out some crucial info? Help is at hand with these sites.

www.scoot.co.uk
THE SIMPLE WAY TO FIND SOMEONE

☺☺☺☺☺

COUNTRY UK

Register, then type in the person's name, hit the scoot button and your answer comes back in seconds.

www.yell.co.uk
THE YELLOW PAGES ON-LINE – JUST YELL!

☺☺☺☺

COUNTRY UK

Split into five main services, but the one you really want is the search engine. You search for the service you want by region, type or name. It is very quick, and you get plenty of details on each entry. There are also sections on travel, property, business and of course, shopping (consisting of a directory for on-line stores covering mainstream merchandise). There is an equivalent service in the USA with the great name of **www.bigfoot.com**.

www.thomweb.co.uk
THE ANSWER COMES OUT OF THE BLUE

☺☺☺☺   Thomson's local directories are available on-line.

COUNTRY UK   It's an impressive site but it's a shame it's so slow. The people finder section has e-mail addresses as well as phone numbers. It's also got all this other stuff:

1. Business finder – search using a combination of name, type of business or region
2. Local information on the major cities and regions
3. 5-day weather forecasts
4. Net Community with sections on chat sites, personal ads, news groups and on-line events.

www.phonenumbers.net
THE PHONE NUMBER OF VIRTUALLY EVERYONE WHO'S LISTED

☺☺☺☺   Start by clicking on the country or area you

COUNTRY
Europe   need, then you can easily find the phone, fax or e-mail address of anyone who is in the book. It also has a section with a number of links to other search engines such as Yell.

Lastly, **www.bt.com/phonenetuk/** takes you right to the on-line phone book.

Sci-Fi and fantasy

Here's all the stuff from outer space, full of aliens, film previews, stories and gossip, oh and Harry Potter.

www.scifi.com
THE SCI-FI CHANNEL

☺☺☺

COUNTRY USA

OK so the TV channel might not be that great but the web site is a different thing altogether. In addition to information about what's on, there are reviews, books, features on characters, music, trailers of forthcoming series and films. The store doesn't supply to the UK.

www.startrek.com
OFFICIAL STAR TREK SITE

☺☺☺☺☺

COUNTRY USA

A really brilliant site for trekkies, there's masses of information on the original and all the spin-off series, with profiles of the characters, technology and aliens.

www.starwars.com
OFFICIAL STAR WARS SITE

☺☺☺

COUNTRY USA

A cool-looking site which is easy to navigate. It's got features on all the films so far plus interviews with George Lucas and the cast. You can get a sneak preview of the next film by paying a visit to the location where they're shooting. You can also view classic *Star Wars* moments and get information on the technology, the planets and aliens.

Other sci-fi TV web sites:

http://babylon5.warnerbros.com
www.buffyslayer.com
www.stargate-sg1.com
www.thexfiles.com
www.mca.com/tv/xena

www.the11thhour.com

☺☺☺☺   11TH HOUR SCI-FI MAGAZINE

COUNTRY USA   A good sci-fi magazine, which offers all a true fan really needs, with review sections on films, books, comics and TV. It can all be a bit serious though. For a less attractive magazine, but more coverage check out www.space.com/sciencefiction/.

www.eonmagazine.com

☺☺☺☺   HOME OF THE MOTHERSHIP

COUNTRY USA   Eon is another magazine site with all the usual reviews and features but with the addition of a very good on-line gaming section, which costs $9.95 a month for unlimited access.

www.sci-fi.co.uk

☺☺☺   SCI-FI SHOP

COUNTRY UK   A huge selection of merchandise is available from all the major sci-fi and fantasy series, as well as background information and pictures on each one. The site design isn't very helpful, and watch out for high delivery charges.

www.voyager-books.com
TRAVELLERS OF THE IMAGINATION

☺ ☺ ☺
COUNTRY UK

Great looking web site from one of the largest UK book publishers, who offer all the Tolkien and George RR Martin titles for sale amongst others. It's great for interviews and features and the odd competition, but you'll find the books cheaper at other booksellers.

www.orbitbooks.co.uk
THE WORLD OF ORBIT

☺ ☺ ☺
COUNTRY UK

Orbit are publishers of Sci-Fi and fantasy in the UK, so it's a great place to visit if you want to keep up-to-date with what's on the way. There's info on current books and author interviews too.

www.ufbs.co.uk/dwm
DISCWORLD MONTHLY

☺ ☺ ☺ ☺
COUNTRY UK

Fans of Terry Pratchett can get their fix of all things on Discworld here. Terry's official site at **www.discworld.com** is under construction at time of writing this, but here there's features, discussion, interviews and much more so why wait?

www.lordoftherings.net
ENTER MIDDLE EARTH

☺ ☺ ☺ ☺ ☺   This is the official film site, which although

COUNTRY UK   takes ages to download is worth a visit as it's
one of the best looking sites around. It has all
the background you need and the film company
keep topping it up with informationand snippets
from the forthcoming feature. There's also links
to other sites, chats and shopping. For games try
www.lysator.liv.se/tolkien-games/. See also
www.thehobbit.org which is also good looking
and offers a huge amount of info on all things
Tolkein.

Harry potter

There are loads of Harry Potter web sites
springing up; here are the official ones and the
best unofficial ones as well. You might want
to keep checking the Warner Brothers site for
information on the forthcoming film –
www.warnerbros.com.

www.bloomsbury.com/harrypotter
WHERE IT ALL BEGAN

☺ ☺ ☺   You have to enter using a secret password

COUNTRY UK   known only to witches and wizards everywhere
then you get to find out all about the books,
meet JK Rowling and join the Harry Potter club.
Don't worry if you're a muggle, all is explained.

www.scholastic.com/harrypotter
HARRY AMERICAN STYLE
☺ ☺

COUNTRY USA

Here's wizard trivia, screensavers, information about the books and an interview with JK Rowling, all on a fairly boring web site.

www.dailyprophetnews.com
THE DAILY PROPHET NEWS
☺ ☺ ☺ ☺

COUNTRY UK

An unofficial newspaper featuring all that goes on in the world of Harry Potter, there's articles, book reviews, features on wizard life and classified ads too.

www.fandom.com/harrypotter
HARRY POTTER FAN CLUB
☺ ☺ ☺ ☺

COUNTRY USA

Everything a fan could want, there's news on the forthcoming books and film, articles, features and polls on all things Harry. The emphasis is on selling you Potter merchandise though so you have to put up with lots of adverts.

Shopping

To many people shopping is the coolest thing about the internet, and if you've been allowed out with the credit card you can get some great bargains. Here are some great shops, but first The Cool Web Site Guide's *top tips to shopping safely.*

1. Keep to recommended shops or well-known brand names.
2. Print and keep all your receipts and documentation.
3. It may be a pain, but read all the small print, there may be terms and conditions that otherwise you're unaware of.
4. Make sure the server is secure before handing over any credit card details. A little padlock will appear in the status bar, or you can check by right clicking on the page and selecting Properties.
5. E-mail is not secure so never use it to give credit card details.
6. Never reveal your passwords or make them too obvious, like using your pet's name for instance.
7. If others use your computer, make sure they can't access information on your passwords

(by looking through the browser's history file for example).

8. Be wary if the store asks for masses of information about you.

9. If you're not sure, then just go to another site, there's bound to be one.

10. Watch out for hidden costs such as delivery charges or finance deals that seem attractive until you compare them with what's available elsewhere. If buying from abroad, there could be local taxes and import duties to be paid.

One of the best places to start is at the *Which? Magazine* Web site, www.which.net, who run a scheme to protect on-line shoppers. They sign up retailers to a code of practice that covers the way they trade. We'll indicate with this symbol – W?WT the sites listed that are part of the scheme and follow the code of practice. You can get a complete list from the *Which?* web site.

www.y-creds.co.uk
NO CREDIT CARD NEEDED

☺☺☺☺☺ Trying to solve the problem of teens not having

COUNTRY UK access to a credit card. You or your parents buy Y-Creds, then you can shop in the Y Street where there are over a hundred stores including high street names who will accept Y-Creds as payment. Brilliant. W?WT

Price checkers

There are many book, music and video price comparison sites; one of the best is at **www.shopsmart.co.uk**; however, the sites listed here allow you to check the prices for on-line stores across a much wider range of merchandise. It's worth trying one or two if you really want the best prices.

www.kelkoo.com
COMPARE PRICES BEFORE YOU BUY

☺☺☺☺☺

COUNTRY
EUROPE

Kelkoo has a good-looking, easy-to-use and well-designed site where you can check prices in 13 key sections including mobile phones, games, books, CDs and videos. There are also product and shop reviews and lists of the latest bargains. Once you've selected what you want to buy, you quickly get put through to the shop that stocks it.

www.checkaprice.com
CONSTANTLY CHECKING PRICES

☺☺☺☺

COUNTRY UK

Compare prices across nearly sixty different product types, from books to cars, holidays, mortgages and electrical goods. If checkaprice can't do it for you, it patches you through to a site that can. It's also worth checking out **www.priceoffers.co.uk** who have a great bargains section.

You could also try **www.price-search.net** who cover computers and electrical goods as well, as do **www.pricewatch.com**.

www.mytaxi.co.uk
SHOP AND SEARCH FOR THE BEST PRICES
☺ ☺ ☺
COUNTRY UK

Personalise your on-line shopping experience using My Taxi to search retailer's web sites for the best prices. Really strong on music and video, less so on other stuff. The recommended on-line stores are selected according to safety and service.

The High Street

The familiar high street names have all jumped on the internet bandwagon; these are the best of them on-line.

www.boots.co.uk
☺ ☺ ☺
COUNTRY UK

A bit of a boring site from Boots aimed at women but with a section for men. The site is split into two sections: Information covers health and beauty plus product news; while The Shop provides an excellent product range under sections covering health and beauty as well as mother and baby. Delivery is free for orders over £60 below that there is a £2.95 charge.

www.whsmith.co.uk

COUNTRY UK

Smiths are a family Internet Service Provider (ISP) which is reflected in the way the site looks – there's loads here divided into several sections. The shopping section has offers on books in particular, but also on CDs, videos and games. (Delivery charges differ between product types.) News covers entertainment, sports and the book world. There's information on computer technology and the internet. You'll find an excellent section for your homework plus the Hutchinson Encyclopaedia. Lastly, hints and tips on lifestyle with good links to health, gardening and other similar sites.

www.argos.co.uk

COUNTRY UK

Argos offers an excellent range of products across fourteen different categories – just like their catalogue. There are some good bargains to be had but you have to search them out. Delivery is £3.95 unless you spend more than £150 in which case it's free.

www.dubit.co.uk
RECOMMENDATIONS

☺☺☺   Not so much a store as a teen magazine that is

COUNTRY UK   good at getting other teenagers to recommend
and comment on the hippest and coolest products. Pretty good magazine too.

The internet's general retailers and department stores

www.shopsmart.com
ON-LINE SHOPPING MADE SIMPLE

☺☺☺☺   This is by far the best of the sites that offer links

COUNTRY UK   to specialist on-line retailers. Search within the
sixteen categories or the whole site for a particular item or store. Each of the 1,000 or so retail
sites featured are reviewed and rated using a star
system, the reviews are quite kind, and the worst
sites are excluded anyway. Use their PriceScan
system to locate the best prices.

See also www.i-stores.co.uk,
www.shopandsave.com, www.2020shops.co.uk
and www.shopspy.co.uk which specialise in
monitoring stores and highlighting those which
are the safest to use and give the best discounts.

www.streetsonline.co.uk
PROBABLY THE UK'S MOST VISITED SITE

☺☺☺☺☺
COUNTRY UK
Books, music, DVD and games are what Streetsonline do best. It's easy-to-use, secure and well-organised. You can also exchange stuff in Xchangestreet. If you have a WAP phone you can also get access to the site and buy stuff. As with most shops you have to register and set up an account first.

www.zoom.co.uk
MORE THAN JUST A SHOP

☺☺☺☺
COUNTRY UK
A really cool, young magazine-style site, with lots of features other than shopping, such as free internet access, e-mail and a dating service. Shopping consists of links to specialist retailers. You can earn loyalty points, enter prize draws and there are a number of exclusive offers as well. Not always the cheapest, but one of the most entertaining.

www.virgin.net
LIFESTYLE AND SHOPPING GUIDE

☺☺☺☺☺
COUNTRY UK
Virgin's shopping guide covers all the major categories while allowing other retailers to feature some of their best offers. It's a complete service for your entertainment and leisure needs with totally brilliant sections on music, travel and cinema in particular.

www.shoppingunlimited.co.uk
INDEPENDENT RECOMMENDATION

☺☺☺

COUNTRY UK

Owned by the *Guardian* newspaper, this site offers hundreds of links to stores that they've reviewed. It also offers help to inexperienced shoppers and guidance on using credit cards on-line. There are also links to other *Guardian* sites such as news and sport.

www.letsbuyit.com
SAVE BY CO-BUYING

☺☺☺

COUNTRY UK

The idea is that by buying in a group you can drive the price down of the products you request. It's great if you can get your friends and family together and you all want to buy the same thing – which is also the downside, you all have the same thing. Prices often aren't that keen either. Still, it's getting better all the time.

www.ybag.com
LET SOMEONE ELSE DO THE SHOPPING

☺☺☺

COUNTRY UK

Can't be bothered with searching the shops? Tell the Ybag team what you want and what you want to pay, and then they put a seller in touch with you. As long as you don't put in requests at silly prices you won't be disappointed, but be prepared for a wait.

Specialist shops

If you don't want to go to a general store, then here's a list of the best specialists in alphabetical order by product.

ART

www.artrepublic.com
BOOKS, POSTERS AND WHAT'S ON

☺ ☺ ☺ ☺

COUNTRY UK

A nicely designed, easy-to-use site, which features three sections:

1. Posters – choose from over 1,500 posters, use the glossary of art terms or peruse artist's biographical data
2. Books – read reviews or select from over 30,000 books. Delivery costs £3 for anywhere
3. What's on where – details of the latest exhibitions, competitions and travel information in London.

www.postershop.co.uk
FINE ART PRINTS AND POSTERS

☺ ☺ ☺ ☺

COUNTRY UK

There are over 20,000 prints and posters available to buy, covering the work of over 100 artists. It has a good search facility that is a bit slow but easy-to-use. Delivery costs £5.

Check out **www.barewalls.com**, which has loads of great posters but watch out for high delivery charges.

www.cass-arts.co.uk

ONE STOP SHOP FOR ART MATERIALS

☺ ☺ ☺
COUNTRY UK

A huge range of art and craft products available to buy on-line, also hints and tips and step-by-step guides, there is an on-line gallery and a section with art trivia and games. The shop has a decent search engine which copes with over 10,000 items, delivery is charged according to what you spend.

BIKES

www.bicyclenet.co.uk

UK'S NUMBER 1 ON-LINE BICYCLE SHOP

☺ ☺ ☺
COUNTRY UK

Great selection of bikes and accessories to buy with free delivery to anywhere in the UK. There's also good advice on how to buy the right bike and they're flexible about the method of payment.

BOOKS

www.bookbrain.co.uk

BEST PRICES FOR BOOKS

☺ ☺ ☺ ☺
COUNTRY UK

All you do is type in the title of the book and Bookbrain will search out the on-line store that is offering it at the lowest price (including postage). You then click again to get taken to the store to buy the book – simple. Access through WAP as well.

To be honest all the on-line bookstores are good,
it's just a matter of taste, here's a list:

www.amazon.co.uk – great on recommendation
  and information
http://bookshop.blackwell.co.uk – helpful, good
  for students
www.bol.com – good site, especially for foreign
  language stuff
www.bookpeople.co.uk – bargains by the ton
www.bookshop.co.uk – good design and links
www.borders.com – good offers, American
www.okukbooks.com – specialises in children's
  books
www.ottakars.co.uk – collect from your local
  store (W?WT)
www.talkingbooks.co.uk – specialises in books
  on tape
www.specialistbooks.co.uk – medical, legal,
  business and science
www.sportspages.com – sport books
www.studentbookworld.com – good offers on
  textbooks (W?WT)
www.waterstones.co.uk – neat design, good on
  literary stuff.

www.swotbooks.com
LOW COST BOOKS FOR CLEVER DICKS

☺☺☺☺

COUNTRY UK

Claim to have the best prices on the dullest books in the world, but some good deals on best sellers too. Go to SwotXChange which is a dating agency for used textbooks, good if you want to buy or sell. UK delivery £2.40 for orders under £50 then it's free.

www.sportspages.co.uk
TAKING SPORT SERIOUSLY

☺☺☺☺

COUNTRY UK

Book and video specialists, concentrating on sport, they offer a wide range at OK prices. Great for that one thing you've been unable to find, or that special present for Dad.

CDs *see Music section, page 104*

CLASSIFIED AD SITES

www.exchangeandmart.co.uk
THOUSANDS OF ADS, UPDATED DAILY

☺☺☺☺☺

COUNTRY UK

Everything the paper has and more, great bargains on a massive range of goods found with good search facility. It is split into 3 major sections:

1. Motoring, including cars, vans, number plates and finance
2. Home including holidays, DIY and gardening
3. Products for small businesses including computers

You can place an ad or get involved with their on-line auctions

www.loot.com
FREE ADS ON-LINE

Ꙭ Ꙭ Ꙭ Ꙭ

COUNTRY UK

Over 140,000 ads and over 3,000 auctioned items make *Loot* a great place to go for a bargain. It's an interesting site to browse with six major sections covering the usual classified ad subjects supplemented by areas featuring jobs, accommodation and personals. Go to *Loot* café for a chat.

COMPUTING AND SOFTWARE

www.itreviews.co.uk
START HERE TO FIND THE BEST

Ꙭ Ꙭ Ꙭ Ꙭ

COUNTRY UK

A great site to visit to when it's time to write your Christmas wish list. IT Reviews gives unbiased reports, not only on computer products, but also software, games and books too. The site has a good search facility and a quick visit may save you loads of hassle when you come to buy. For other excellent information sites try **www.zdnet.co.uk** or **www.cnet.com**, both have links to good on-line stores.

DVDS *see Movies section, page 100*

FASHION AND CLOTHES
This where it's at guys and gals! Cheap clothes and all the labels you need…

www.adidas.co.uk
GREAT, IF YOU'RE AMERICAN

☺☺

COUNTRY USA

Adidas has a great looking web site with free downloads, but you can't get much at the on-line store unless you're American. What's there can be very expensive.

www.bodyshop.co.uk
THE BODY SHOP

☺☺☺

COUNTRY UK

Balancing the rights of the under-privileged with the demands of a commercial cosmetics company, the Body Shop site has loads of information but you can't buy anything. However, you can download and play with the virtual makeover, which is fun.

www.clairesaccessories.co.uk
WICKED COLOURS, WICKED SHOPPING

☺☺☺☺☺

COUNTRY USA

Wicked Colours is a really cool girls magazine that has tips on make-up, hair and fashion as well as gossip, chat and features. Of course, the whole thing is designed to get you shopping, which has everything from scooters to mobiles to clothes and all those lovely accessories. You have to register to join and you get a welcome pack too.

www.designersdirect.com
THE BIG BRANDS AT HUGE DISCOUNTS

☺☺☺☺

COUNTRY USA

If you are into designer brands, then this excellent site may be all you'll ever need. Split into four major sections: men's, women's, eyewear and footwear, each is clearly laid out with a good quality, large photo of each item. The range is good as are the prices. Delivery charges vary according to what you spend. Also check out **www.designerheaven.co.uk** who offer free world-wide delivery.

www.diesel.co.uk
COOL DESIGN

☺☺☺

COUNTRY UK

Brilliant design and a good choice of the latest clothing from Diesel, delivery is £4 per order.

www.fashionicon.com
HOW TO BE A FASHION ICON

☺☺☺☺

COUNTRY USA

Want to know what's in and what's hot? Then check out Fashion Icon for all the latest fashion news and tips. Check with other icons just what you should be wearing and in what colours too. No shopping but essential if you don't want to be wearing gear that's 'so last week'.

http://girlsgottashop.com

A GIRLS GOTTA DO WHAT A GIRLS GOTTA DO...

☻☻☻☻

COUNTRY UK

Great-looking shop for all those essential accessories, make-up and even jewellery; there's also some excellent bargains. It has a good selection of clothes too.

www.intofashion.com

GET REALLY INTO FASHION

☻☻☻☻☻

COUNTRY UK

With sections on jewellery, hair accessories, scarves, bags and clothes, Intofashion offers a complete service, backed by excellent design and picture quality. You can search the site by designer, product or browse for the best buys. Delivery is free in the UK. Another similar site is **www.theclothesstore.com** with a good selection of clothes and accessories, but a charge for delivery to the UK.

www.kookai.co.uk

BUY KOOKAI

☻☻☻

COUNTRY UK

OK so you have to look like a rake to shop there, but this is a really cool site and the clothes great and expensive, but there's no harm in looking...

www.nike.com
ON YER MARK, GET READY TO SHOP
☺ ☺ ☺

COUNTRY USA Nike's Eurostore has all the Nike products shown on a flashy web site where you can even do things like design your own running shoe, but it can be very slow to use and expensive.

www.noveltytogs.com
FOR CHARACTER MERCHANDISE
☺ ☺ ☺ ☺

COUNTRY UK Some people get a kick from wearing clothes with their fave TV characters plastered all over them. If you're one of them go here for Simpsons, South Park, Garfield and Peanuts. There are the usual T-shirts plus boxer shorts, socks and night-shirts. Delivery is free for the UK and there are links to other character web sites. W?WT

www.topshop.co.uk
ORDER TODAY SHOW OFF TOMORROW
☺ ☺ ☺ ☺

COUNTRY UK A fast and flash site for Topshop with lots of the latest fashions, next day delivery for orders placed before 3pm and a no quibble refund policy. Standard shipping charge is £1.95.

www.ukdesignershop.com
GUYS – DRESS SMART FOR LESS
☺ ☺ ☺ ☺ ☺

COUNTRY UK Great clothes and great prices, on a really well-designed web site. It's easy-to-use and there's a good returns policy.

GAMES *see Games section, page 51*

GIFTS

www.lastminute.com
NOT JUST HOLIDAYS
☺☺☺☺☺   This is one of the most famous web sites, better

COUNTRY UK   known for travel; however, it has a great section
          for gifts too, with a really cool selection. There's
          also help on hand to find the right gift.

www.asseenonscreen.com
WEAR WHAT THE CELEBRITIES WEAR
☺☺☺☺   Now you can buy that bit of jewellery or cool

COUNTRY UK   gear that you saw Buffy or Angel wearing, As
          Seen on Screen specialises in supplying just
          that. Cheap it ain't but you'll get noticed.
          You can request products too so if you've seen
          something you really must have, they'll try to
          get it for you.

www.stuckforagift.com
CAN'T THINK WHAT TO BUY?
☺☺☺   Stuck for a Gift have a fairly boring web site,

COUNTRY UK   but they do have masses of unusual gifts and
          they deliver quickly and free if you spend
          more than a tenner. The best place to start is

the catalogue section where you get thumbnail images of everything they stock, be patient though, it takes a while to download. W?WT

HUMOUR

www.jokeshopfun.com
EVERYTHING YOU NEED TO PLAY TRICKS

☺ ☺ ☺

COUNTRY UK

Jokes, masks and magic it's all here and the web site is fun too. Each of the products is pictured and there's a note about what age it's suitable for. Delivery is £1.

JEWELLERY

www.jewellers.net
THE BIGGEST RANGE ON THE NET

☺ ☺ ☺

COUNTRY UK

Excellent range of products including fashion jewellery, gifts, gold and silver, and the watch section is particularly good. There is also information on the history of gems, the manufacturers and brands available. Delivery to the UK is free and there is a 30 day no quibble returns policy. W?WT

www.hpj.co.uk

HALF PRICE JEWELLERS

☺☺☺☺   The UK's leading discount jeweller offers a
COUNTRY UK   cheap, reliable service with delivery being £2.95
per order, with next day service at £4.95.
Excellent prices compared to the high street.

MAGAZINES

www.britishmagazines.com

BRITISH MAGAZINES DIRECT

☺☺☺☺   Order just about any UK magazine and get it
COUNTRY UK   delivered to your home free of charge. Its fast
and easy-to-use, but you have to register. See
also **www.whsmith.co.uk**.

MAKE-UP

www.lookfantastic.com

LOOK GREAT AND SAVE MONEY

☺☺☺☺   Up to 60% discount on all sorts of different
COUNTRY UK   types of make-up and beauty products,
everything from cosmetics, shampoo and even
accessories. Check out **www.beauty4you.co.uk**
as an alternative.

MOBILES *see separate Phones and phone numbers section, page 137*

MOVIES *see Movies section, page 100*

MUSIC STUFF *see Music and radio section, page 104*

PARTY STUFF

www.thepartystore.co.uk
SELLING FUN

☺☺☺ Having a bash? These guys sell character outfits,
COUNTRY UK themed tableware, masks, party boxes and all
sorts of accessories. Delivery takes 4 working days
and cost £2.95 or free if you spend £40 or more.

PERFUME

www.fragrancenet.com
WORLD'S LARGEST DISCOUNT FRAGRANCE STORE

☺☺☺ A massive range of perfumes for men and
COUNTRY USA women, every brand is represented and there are
some excellent offers. However, the site is
American with shipping costs of up to $23
dollars for 5 items or more. Also check out
www.island-trading.com who have a big selection of perfumes and cosmetics.

PET SHOPS *see separate Pet section, page 133*

PHONES *see separate Phones and phone numbers section, page 137*

SHOES

www.shoe-shop.com

☺☺☺☺☺ Shoes yeah!

COUNTRY UK   One of the best shops on the net, good design, easy-to-use and great service too. There's loads to choose from, each shoe can be seen from several angles and there's a really good returns facility. Delivery is free. See also **www.shoesdirect.co.uk**

If you're really fashion-conscious go for **www.ozzys.co.uk** who have all the right brands. The web site isn't that great though.

STATIONERY

www.office-supplies.co.uk

☺☺☺ Stationery on-line

COUNTRY UK   Up to 14,000 items available, and if you place an order before 5.30 pm, you get free next day delivery providing you spend over £35. It's really aimed at business users but if you need to buy a

lot of stationery this is a good bet.
See also **www.harperoffice.co.uk** and
www.whsmith.co.uk.

SOFTWARE

www.softwareparadise.co.uk
THE SMART WAY TO SHOP FOR SOFTWARE

☺☺☺☺   With over 250,000 titles and excellent offers
COUNTRY UK   make this site your first stop. It's easy-to-use and
there's a good search facility and plenty of prod-
ucts for Mac users. There are links to sister sites
offering low cost software for charities and
students. W?WT If you feel like shopping around
check out:
www.software-warehouse.co.uk W?WT
www.beyond.com
www.zdnet.com.

SPORTSWEAR

www.kitbag.com
SPORTS FASHION

☺☺☺☺   Football kits and gear galore from new to retro;
COUNTRY UK   covers cricket and rugby too. Free delivery.

www.discountsports.co.uk

UK'S LOWEST PRICED SPORTSWEAR

☺ ☺ ☺ ☺

COUNTRY UK

Cheap and cheerful approach, with all the major brands represented and much of what they offer has free delivery in the UK. W?WT

www.fatface.co.uk

FASHION LEISURE AND SPORTS WEAR

☺ ☺ ☺ ☺

COUNTRY UK

Want to look cool when you play sport? Here's where to go for great sports clothes for all ages.

TOYS AND BOXED GAMES

www.etoys.co.uk

FANTASTIC TOY SHOP

☺ ☺ ☺ ☺ ☺

COUNTRY UK

An excellent site featuring not just toys, but also software, games and videos, very easy-to-use and regularly tops customer service polls – there's even a price promise. Great for character stuff and has a section that categorises toys by age. W?WT If you can't find something here try one of these:

www.funstore.co.uk

www.toysrus.co.uk

www.discounttoys.co.uk.

Sport

Keep up-to-date with how your team is performing, or if you're a member of a team or association, keep each other updated. There's also a list of good places to visit if you want to look the part.

General sports sites

www.sporting-life.com
THE SPORTING LIFE
☺☺☺☺

COUNTRY UK

Bags of advice, tips, news and the latest scores, it's considered to be one of the best, and it's very good for stories, statistics, and overall coverage of the major sports.

www.sports.com
SPORTS – WELL SORTED
☺☺☺☺

COUNTRY UK

More international than Sporting Life, it's got loads of info on all the important sports, particularly football, along with a shopping service mainly covering cricket, football and golf.

www.sky.com/sports/home/
THE BEST OF SKY SPORT

☺☺☺☺
COUNTRY UK

Great for the Premiership and football in general, but also covers other sports very well, particularly cricket and both forms of rugby. Includes a section featuring video and audio clips, and interviews with stars. You can vote in their polls or try sports trivia quizzes.

www.talksport.net
HOME OF TALK SPORT RADIO

☺☺☺☺
COUNTRY UK

Check out the latest sports news while you do your homework, the information comes from Sporting Life but it's really up-to-date. There's also an audio archive and scheduling information.

The BBC keeps up the good work with great sports coverage from their own web site **www.bbc.co.uk/sport**.

Athletics

www.athletix.gr
WORLD ATHLETICS NEWS

☺☺☺☺
COUNTRY UK

A really cool site that is comprehensive and easy-to-use. There are reports on each Grand Prix and event, with statistics and links to other specialist sites. To see what Linford Christie is up to these days go to **www.nuff-respect.co.uk**.

Basketball

www.nba.com
NATIONAL BASKETBALL ASSOCIATION

☺ ☺ ☺
COUNTRY USA

The official site, with features on the teams, players and games; there's also a fantastic photo gallery and you can watch replays of some of the most important points if you have the right software.

For British basketball go to www.bbl.org.uk, or www.britball.com which is unofficial but more of a laugh.

Boxing (not suitable for younger children)

www.boxingonline.com
AT THE RINGSIDE

☺ ☺ ☺ ☺
COUNTRY USA

A combination of information and the latest technology make this a really cool web-site. There's also interviews, news and feature stories as well as events listings. You can download fight extracts in both audio and video formats.

Check out these sites for the all the different boxing authorities:

WBA – www.wbaonline.com

WBC – www.ajapa.qc.ca/wbc/index/html

WBF – www.worldboxingfed.com

WBU – www.btinternet.com/wbuboxing/

For women's boxing go to www.femboxer.com.

www.houseofboxing.com
HOME FOR BOXING ON THE NET
☺☺☺☺   A wickedly designed site that covers the world of
COUNTRY USA   boxing, including video interviews, reviews and
features.

Cricket

www.uk.cricket.org or www.cricinfo.com
THE HOME OF CRICKET ON THE NET
☺☺☺☺   Probably the best cricket site in the world, it's
COUNTRY UK   got loads of analysis, match reports, player
profiles, statistics, links to other more specialised
sites and live written commentary. There's also a
shop with lots of cricket goodies, delivery is
included in the price.

www.khel.com
WORLD CRICKET
☺☺☺☺   Another site for the mega cricket fan, it's partic-
COUNTRY   ularly good for looking up statistics whether it is
INDIA   on players or matches, and it has a good set of
links to other cricket sites.

www.wisden.com
WISDEN CRICKET MONTHLY
☺☺☺☺   The best features from Wisden's Cricket
COUNTRY UK   Magazine, created in association with the
Guardian newspaper and its excellent site

www.cricketunlimited.co.uk, which has some of
the best writing on cricket you can get.

www.lords.org
THE OFFICIAL LINE ON CRICKET

☻☻☻☻
COUNTRY UK

There's news, links to governing bodies, associations and the MCC and ECB, combined with
plenty of information about the game and players, even a quiz. It also has an excellent section
on women's cricket. If you have RealPlayer,
there's access to live games on audio via the
BBC.

www.webbsoc.demon.co.uk
WOMEN'S CRICKET ON THE WEB

☻☻
COUNTRY UK

There are not many sites about women's cricket,
this is probably the best, with features, news,
fixture lists, match reports and player profiles.
Nothing fancy, but whatever, it works.

Cycling

www.bcf.uk.com/
BRITISH CYCLING FEDERATION

☻☻
COUNTRY UK

The governing body for cycling, the site is under
development but you can still get information on
events, rules, clubs and rankings.

www.bikemagic.com
IT'S BIKETASTIC!

☺☺☺☺ Plenty of news and features, as well as reviews
COUNTRY UK on bike parts and gadgets. There's also a
classified ads section and a selection of links to
other biking web sites all of which are rated.

Equestrian

www.equestrianonline.com
CLIPPITY CLOP

☺☺☺☺ Get all the news and results on the sport plus
COUNTRY UK articles by those involved, profiles of the riders,
owners and trainers, training tips and forums on
each event; there's a bookstore too.

Fishing

www.fishing.org
HOME OF UK FISHING ON THE NET – SPLASH!

☺☺☺☺ A humungous site that has information on
COUNTRY UK where to fish, how to fish, where's the best place
to stay near fish, even fishing holidays. There's
also advice on equipment, a records section and
links to shops and shop locations.

Shop on-site for fishing books and
magazines. See also **www.anglersnet.co.uk**
for good writing and for more information
www.services-online.co.uk/angling.

Football

www.footballnews.co.uk
IT'S ALL HERE

☺☺☺☺

COUNTRY UK

If you want a site that covers everything, this is hard to beat. It's easier to use than most other football sites; it's also up-to-date and doesn't miss much.

www.kidzunited.com
TOP FOOTY

☺☺☺☺☺

COUNTRY UK

Bex and friends are Kidz United and will guide you through the site. There is masses to do and see – news, competitions, interviews, quizzes and much more.

See also www.football365.co.uk and www.soccerage.com and www.soccernet.com which are excellent for world football; for good sports writing try www.footballunlimited.co.uk; for a laugh go to www.zoofootball.com which is a bit rude.

www.ukfootballpages.com
HELP – WHERE DO I FIND FOOTBALL?

☺☺☺

COUNTRY UK

This site offers a huge directory of football-related links and boasts some 1200 enquiries a day; also offers match reports and statistics.

www.teamtalk.com
CHECK OUT THE LATEST GOSS

☺☺☺☺
COUNTRY UK

The place to go if you want all the latest gossip and transfer information, it's opinionated but not often wrong.

Golf

www.golftoday.co.uk
THE BEST ON-LINE GOLF MAGAZINE

☺☺☺☺
COUNTRY UK

A bit dry, but an excellent site for golf news and tournaments with features, statistics, rankings and a course directory, it's the best all-round site covering Europe. There are also links to sister sites about the amateur game, shops and where to stay.

www.golfweb.com
PGA TOUR

☺☺☺☺
COUNTRY USA

Great for statistics on the game and keeping up with tournament scores. It also has audio and visual features with RealPlayer. For the official word on the tour go to **www.pga.com**.

Hockey

www.fieldhockey.com
HOCKEY NEWS

☺☺☺☺
COUNTRY UK

All the information, news and games round-ups; there's also good archive stuff, up-to-date rules and sections for coaches. For lots of hockey links go to **http://hockey.enschede.com/uk/links.htm**.

Horse racing

www.racingpost.co.uk
THE RACING POST

☺☺☺☺
COUNTRY UK
Loads of info from the most knowledgeable people, every event covered in-depth with tips and advice. To get the best out of it you have to register, then you gain access to the database and more. For more information on the sport go to the British Horse Racing Board's excellent site at **www.bhb.co.uk**.

Ice hockey

www.iceweb.co.uk
THE SEKONDA ICE HOCKEY LEAGUE

☺☺☺
COUNTRY UK
Keep up-to-date with the scores, the games and the players – even their injuries. Good for statistics as well as news. For more news see also **www.azhockey.com** – Coooelll!

www.nhl.com
NATIONAL HOCKEY LEAGUE

☺☺☺
COUNTRY USA
Check out the latest from the NHL including a chance to listen and watch key moments from past and recent games.

Martial arts

www.martial-arts-network.com
PROMOTING MARTIAL ARTS

☺☺   Possibly qualifies as the loudest introduction

COUNTRY USA sequence, but once you've cut the volume, the
             site has loads of information about the martial
             arts scene; sadly it's slow and a little confusing
             to use.

Motor sport

www.ukmotorsport.com
INFORMATION OVERLOAD

☺☺☺☺   This site covers every form of motor racing; it's

COUNTRY UK   easy-to-use and doesn't miss anything, with lots
             of links to other motor sport sites.

www.linksheaven.com
LINKS AND LINKS AND MORE LINKS AND...

☺☺☺☺   Whatever, whoever, there's a link to the right

COUNTRY USA web site. It generally concentrates on Formula 1,
             CART and Nascar though.

www.autosport.com
AUTOSPORT MAGAZINE

☺☺☺   Really excellent for news and features on motor

COUNTRY UK   sport plus links and a slightly confusing on-line
             shop where you can get related products such as
             team gear, books or models.

www.rallysport.com
COVERING THE WORLD RALLY CHAMPIONSHIP
☺☺☺☺

COUNTRY UK

Great for results and news on rallying across the world and in the UK. See also www.rallyzone.co.uk which is very good.

www.btcc.co.uk
BRITISH TOURING CAR CHAMPIONSHIP
☺☺☺☺

COUNTRY UK

A really wicked site with loads of stuff on the championship, drivers and teams, also photos and links to other related sites.

www.fosa.org
FORMULA ONE SUPPORTERS ASSOCIATION
☺☺☺☺

COUNTRY UK

This has been set up by fans to provide feedback to the people who run Formula 1. There are quizzes, statistics and articles, even a tour of a racing car.

www.itv-f1.com
F1 ON ITV
☺☺☺☺☺

COUNTRY UK

This web site is excellent. There's carloads of action, with all the background information you need, plus circuit profiles, schedules and a photo gallery. For more news and links to everywhere in F1 go to www.f1-world.co.uk.

Mountaineering and outdoor sports

www.mountainzone.com
UPWARDLY MOBILE

☺☺☺☺ Covers all aspects of climbing, hiking, mountain

COUNTRY USA biking, skiing and snowboarding – phew! It's got
a very good photography section featuring
galleries of mountains and climbers. There's a
store offering gear at discount prices, shipping is
expensive though so you'll save by visiting
www.rockandrun.co.uk.

Rugby

www.scrum.com
RUGBY UNION

☺☺☺☺ A really good site about rugby union with up-to-

COUNTRY UK the-minute coverage – it's amazing how quick
they are. It's a bit serious though, so go to
www.planet-rugby.com if you want a laugh.

www.rugbyrugby.com
WORLD RUGBY

☺☺☺☺ Amazing round up of world rugby with instant

COUNTRY reports, lots of detail and information on both
NEW ZEALAND union and league. There's also a shop with a
small selection of gear, which is very expensive
when you add delivery charges.

www.irb.org/
INTERNATIONAL RUGBY BOARD

☺ ☺ ☺
COUNTRY UK

For the official line on rugby union, there's the rules and regulations explained, information on world tournaments, history of the game and some good articles from *Oval World* magazine.

www.rleague.com
WORLD OF RUGBY LEAGUE

☺ ☺ ☺ ☺
COUNTRY UK

Truckloads of info, featuring sections on Australia, New Zealand and the UK, with plenty of chat, articles, player profiles and enough statistics to keep the maddest fan happy.

Skiing and snowboarding

www.fis-ski.com
INTERNATIONAL SKI FEDERATION

☺ ☺ ☺
COUNTRY USA

Catch up on the news, the fastest times and the rankings in all forms of skiing at this site. Very good background information and an excellent picture gallery sets the whole thing off. Brrr.

www.natives.co.uk
THE COOLEST NATIVES OF THE MOUNTAINS

☺ ☺ ☺
COUNTRY UK

The most happening of ski sites with information on conditions, ski resorts, jobs, where to stay and links to other cool sites all wrapped up in a wicked design.

www.snowboardinguk.co.uk
UK SNOWBOARDING NEWS

☺☺☺☺

COUNTRY UK

A surprisingly uncool site for what is after all the coolest of sports. Aimed at anyone whether beginner or expert, it has news, an events diary, resort information, travel information and a links page.

Feel the Powder www.feelthepow.com looks good but isn't really, for shopping try www.legendsboardriders.com.

Snooker

www.snookernet.com
ALL ABOUT SNOOKER

☺☺☺☺

COUNTRY UK

Easy-to-use site that has lots of information on the game, plus tips from a top player, links, a shop selling snooker stuff, a club finder and subscription to *SnookerScene* magazine.

Tennis and racquet sports

www.lta.org.uk
LAWN TENNIS ASSOCIATION

☺☺☺☺☺

COUNTRY UK

A brilliant tennis information site run by the Lawn Tennis Association, it has information on the players, rankings and tournament news, as well as details on clubs and coaching courses. See also www.atptour.com which is more international.

www.tennis.org.uk
THE TENNIS SEARCH ENGINE

☺☺☺☺
COUNTRY UK

You can search a mass of good tennis links, plus get all the results information and stats. It's also very easy-to-use.

www.wimbledon.org
THE OFFICIAL WIMBLEDON SITE

☺☺☺
COUNTRY UK

Very impressive, but slow, there's loads here though. Apart from the information, you can download screensavers of the players, visit the on-line museum and see videos of past matches. The shop is expensive.

www.badmintonuk.ndo.co.uk
BRITISH BADMINTON

☺☺☺☺
COUNTRY UK

A clear, easy-to-use site packed with information about badminton, how ladders work, directory of coaches, club directory, rules, but not much news on the game. For that go to www.baofe.co.uk, the site of the badminton association of England. For a bit of attitude try www.realbadminton.co.uk .

www.squashplayer.co.uk
WORLD OF SQUASH

☺☺☺☺
COUNTRY UK

An OK round up of the game, with loads of links and a great news section, there's also a section for the UK, which has club details and the latest news.

www.ettu.org
EUROPEAN TABLE TENNIS UNION

☺☺☺ COUNTRY UK — Find out about the ETTU, it's rankings, competition details and results plus a section devoted to world table tennis links. See also www.ittf.com, which gives a world view.

Water sports and swimming

www.swimnet.co.uk
ALL YOU NEED TO KNOW ABOUT SWIMMING

☺☺☺ COUNTRY UK — The best site on swimming in the UK, this has details on the major events, news, profiles and videos of the best swimmers and races.

www.stormrider.co.uk
SURFING UK!

☺☺☺ COUNTRY UK — Includes forecasts for weather and surf, satellite images, live surf web cams from around the world and a complete directory of surfing web sites. Try www.surfcall.co.uk as well.

Wrestling (not suitable for young children)

www.wwf.com
WORLD WRESTLING FEDERATION - FULLY LOADED

☺☺☺☺ COUNTRY USA — We'd better not give this a bad review! Really it's a great site with loads of stuff on the wrestlers, news, games, quizzes and information. It's not fixed – honest!

You wanna smell what the Rock is cooking? Check out www.therock.com.

www.wcw.com
WORLD CHAMPIONSHIP WRESTLING
☺ ☺ ☺

COUNTRY USA

Not as popular as WWF and the web site is not as good either! There's lots of news, but it's really about selling their merchandise.

Sporting heroes

Boxing

www.princenaseem.com – Naseem Hamed

Football

www.liverpoolfc.org/gallery/owen.html – Michael Owen

http://beckhamsite.tripod.com – David Beckham

Golf

www.tigerwoods.com – Tiger Woods

Motor sport

www.jensonbuttononline.co.uk – Jenson Button

www.hakkinen.net – Mika Hakkinen

www.exclusivelyirvine.com – Eddy Irvine

www.mschumacher.com – Michael Schumacher

Tennis

www.tim-henman.co.uk – Tim Henman

http://goto.rusedski – Greg Rusedski

www.sampras.com – Pete Sampras

www.kournikova.com – Anna Kournikova

See also www.advantagetennis.com

SPORTS CLOTHES *see separate Sportswear section, page 169*

Students

There is masses of information for students on the net. Here are some worth checking out. The links are generally very good, so if the topic isn't covered here, it should be easy to track down.

Universities and colleges

www.ucas.co.uk
THE UNIVERSITY STARTING BLOCK

☺☺☺☺☺ A comprehensive site listing all the courses at
COUNTRY UK British universities with entry profiles. You can view the directory on-line and order your UCAS handbook and application form. If you've already applied, you can view your application on-line. There are links to all the universities plus excellent links to related sites. There is good advice too.

If you want to study abroad try finding a course through **www.edunet.com**.

www.nusonline.co.uk
STUDENTS UNITE

☺☺☺☺ Lots of relevant news and views for students.
COUNTRY UK You need to register to get assess to their discounts directory and special offers. Once in

you can send postcards and use their mail and
storage facilities too.

www.lineone.net/learning/
START YOUR RESEARCH HERE

☺☺☺   A good offering from Lineone with advice on

COUNTRY UK   loans, career planning and, if you search around,
you'll find info on non-degree vocational train-
ing. Go to Schoolsnet for info on colleges and
universities, a curriculum-based webguide and
help with revision. When checking out universities you can also try *The Times Good University
Guide* www.the-times.co.uk/gug.

www.freefund.com
DEDICATED TO STUDENT SOLVENCY

☺☺☺   A search will reveal whether anyone out there

COUNTRY UK   will help you finance your studies, even if you
are still at school. There's well-informed advice
on student finance issues and you can ask an
expert if you're in a fix.

Working abroad

www.gapyear.com
THE WORLD'S YOUR OYSTER

☺☺☺☺   Whether you fancy helping out in the forests of

COUNTRY UK   Brazil or teaching in Europe you'll find information and opportunities here. There is loads of
advice, past experiences to get you tempted,

chat, bulletin boards, competitions and you can subscribe to their magazine (an old-fashioned paper one).

www.payaway.co.uk
FIND A JOB ABROAD OR WORKING HOLIDAY

☺☺☺☺☺ A great starting place for anyone who wants to
COUNTRY UK work abroad. There is a magazine, reports from travellers and you can register with their on-line jobs service. They've missed nothing out in their links section from embassies to travel health to Durex.

Discount cards

www.istc.org.uk
INTERNATIONAL STUDENT TRAVEL CONFEDERATION

☺☺☺ Get your student and youth discount card as
COUNTRY UK well as info on working and studying abroad. Also help with such things as rail passes, phonecards, ISTC registered travel agents world-wide, plus e-mail, voice mail and fax messaging. For a European youth card for discounts within the EU go to **www.euro26.org**.

Magazines

www.studentuk.com
BEER IS LIFE – THEIR WORDS NOT OURS!

ت ت ت ت ت   A useful and generally well-written student's
COUNTRY UK   magazine featuring news, music and film
reviews, going out, chat, even articles on science
and politics. Some excellent advice on subjects
such as gap years, accommodation, even on
science. It's also worth checking out
www.ragmag.co.uk who continue the tradition
of ragweek all the time, and is a source for all
things good. **www.anythingstudent.com** is also
worth a look although it could be more fun.

Travel

OK so you're getting itchy feet for a year off to go travelling, here's some sites that may just help. Have a look at the sites on working abroad in the Student section too.

www.fco.gov.uk/travel
TRAVEL ADVICE FROM THE FOREIGN OFFICE

☺☺☺☺☺
COUNTRY UK

Before you go anywhere in the world, this is the first site to visit when planning your trip. It will give the latest information on countries with political or economic concerns with advice on safe travelling and links to helpful web sites.

www.lonelyplanet.com
TRAVEL GUIDES FOR THE INDEPENDENT

☺☺☺☺☺
COUNTRY UK

Brilliant web site, which is more than just an on-line guidebook as there's masses of travel information combined with the wisdom of experience. Get a review on most world destinations or pick a theme, leave a message on the thorn tree, find out the latest news by country, get health reports and relive the real travel experiences of others. One of the best services is the eKno system, which is a combined phone, e-mail and answer machine which offers a great way to stay in touch when you're in the back of beyond.

Other good on-line travel guides can be found at either Rough Guides

http://travel.roughguides.com or at the more
American Fodors www.fodors.com.

www.vtourist.com
THE VIRTUAL TOURIST

☺☺☺☺☺

COUNTRY UK

OK, so you can't afford the trip, then become a
virtual tourist! This site allows you to travel the
world using the internet as your transport; it's
simple and fascinating. It's also a great place to
get insider knowledge of places that you're
studying or thinking of visiting and a good way
of meeting people on-line who may be interested
in your part of the world.

www.pgl.co.uk
WHERE THE ADVENTURE BEGINS

☺☺☺

COUNTRY UK

Want something different? PGL specialise in
activity holidays and they have a great selection
here including skiing and adventure trips.
Check out www.activitiesonline.co.uk as a
good alternative.

www.yha.org.uk
YOUTH HOSTEL ASSOCIATION

☺☺☺☺☺

COUNTRY UK

Cheap, good quality accommodation is offered
across England and Wales and you can even make
a booking on-line. There's also plenty of offers
highlighted on the site and you can get details of
their adventure holidays. The site provides a really
good selection of links to helpful sites.

TV

*All the best TV shows and channels have their own web
sites but are they any good? Find out here.*

Channels

www.bbc.co.uk
THE UK'S MOST POPULAR WEB SITE

☺☺☺☺☺ The BBC site is huge and really amazing with
COUNTRY UK   over 300 sections and this review only scrapes
the surface. These are the main sections:

- News – keep up to date with the tickertape
  facility
- Weather – 1, 3 or 5 day forecasts and more
- Sport – catch up on all the scores, news and
  gossip
- Arts – literature, classical and art
- Education – a brilliant section for homework
  with features from many programmes
- Entertainment – catch up on all the favourite
  BBC shows
- Food – recipes from the stars, tips and what's
  healthy
- Gardening – advice and info on plants
- Health – the latest advice and news

- History – features from many history programmes
- Homes – antiques, DIY and inspiration
- Kids – the best of Blue Peter, Newsround and Live & Kicking; also info on the stars, have your say and games
- Live chat – talk to the stars of BBC TV and radio
- Nature – from dinosaurs to frog spawn
- Radio – find out what's on and visit the listening booth
- Science – the latest inventions and discoveries
- Teens – *So* magazine and other cool stuff
- What's on – err what's on
- World Service – sections on world regions, with a live web cast and news bulletins

As you'd expect, the programming leads the tone of each section, and there's the BBC Web Guide that allows you to check on related links. You can also go shopping at the groovier sister site **www.beeb.com**.

www.channel4.co.uk
CHANNEL 4

☺ ☺ ☺

COUNTRY UK

A cool site with details of programmes and links to specific web pages on the best-known ones, there's also links to other initiatives such as Filmfour.

www.channel5.co.uk
CHANNEL 5
☺ ☺ ☺

COUNTRY UK

Similar to Channel 4 except it's got more in the way of games and competitions. It's also a bit clearer and easier to find your way around.

www.citv.co.uk
CHILDREN'S ITV
☺ ☺ ☺

COUNTRY UK

A bright and breezy site that features competitions, chat, safe surfing, features on the programmes including *SM:TV*, and much more. You need to join to get the best out of it though, and because there's so much on the site it can be a little slow.

www.itv.co.uk
ITV NETWORK
☺ ☺ ☺

COUNTRY UK

A pretty straightforward site with links to all the major programmes, their related web sites and a what's on guide.

www.nicktv.co.uk
NICKELODEON
☺ ☺ ☺ ☺

COUNTRY UK

Bright doesn't do this site justice, you need sunglasses! It's got info on all the top programmes; *Sabrina*, *Kenan and Kel* and so on, plus games and quizzes.

www.sky.com
SKY TV

☺☺☺☺
COUNTRY UK
You'd be forgiven for thinking this was a news site, but a closer look reveals that there are links to all the best Sky programmes as well as great features such as games, shopping and links to other sister sites.

www.trouble.co.uk
TROUBLE TV

☺☺☺☺
COUNTRY UK
The home of Young Americans has a cool site with lots to see including show times, chat, radio and features on the shows. The best bit is Flash Boyfriend where you can influence the storylines.

Favourite programmes

www.wb17.com/entertainment/wb/angel
ANGEL

☺☺☺
COUNTRY USA
Buffy spin-off Angel gets his own web site with background notes on the characters, plots and plenty of pictures. You can also play games too.

www.buffyslayer.com
Buffy
☺ ☺ ☺ ☺
COUNTRY USA

Top site for vampire slayers, there's loads to see and do with lots of pictures, games, explanation of the characters, stories, background on the plot and much more. You can select either the hi-tech version or the simpler faster version.

www.dawsons-creek.com
Dawsons Creek
☺ ☺ ☺ ☺
COUNTRY USA

Everything is here, storylines, interviews, chat and feedback as well as the ability for you to send *Dawsons Creek* postcards, learn about Cape Cod and download the music. All packaged on a nice web site.

http://friends.warnerbros.com
Official Friends site
☺ ☺ ☺ ☺
COUNTRY USA

Another great Warner Brothers site with lots of background on the series and the six friends, the site looks fun from the start with games, freebies and a lively chat section. You can even become a 'friend'.

www.paramount.com/tvsistersister
Sister Sister
☺ ☺ ☺
COUNTRY USA

A pretty basic site but there's all the information you'll need on the sisters.

www.marykateandashley.com
MARY-KATE AND ASHLEY

☺☺☺   Massive web site dedicated to the globetrotting
COUNTRY USA   girls with all sorts of stuff from photos, stories
and features to more photos stories and
features…oh and there's a few fashion tips too.

Soaps

www.brookie.com
THE OFFICIAL BROOKSIDE WEB SITE

☺☺☺   You have two options, either the highly
COUNTRY UK   animated version or the one with less pictures
and no sound. Either will give you all the latest
information, gossip or storyline with loads of
background info on the cast. There are competitions and you can shop for Brookie merchandise.
With the animated version you can download
clips and take a virtual tour, but be patient and
the sound effects are really annoying.

www.corrie.net
CORONATION STREET BY ITS FANS

☺☺☺   Corrie was formed in 1999 from several fan
COUNTRY UK   sites and has no connection with Granada. The
site is written by volunteer fans who've
contributed articles, updates and biographies.
There are five key sections. One for Corrie
newbies (are there any?) with a history of the

Street, a catch up with the story section, what's up and coming, profiles on the key characters and a chat section where you can gossip about the goings on. For a another fan's eye view try out www.csvu.net.

www.coronationstreet.co.uk
THE OFFICIAL CORONATION STREET

☺ ☺ ☺ ☺

COUNTRY UK

This is the official site, and its split into several sections including 'classic moments', chats with the star, a virtual tour and even a fantasy game where you can choose your favourite characters to act together. The site is spoiled by too much advertising.

www.emmerdale.co.uk
THE OFFICIAL EMMERDALE SITE

☺ ☺ ☺ ☺

COUNTRY UK

Very similar to the official *Coronation Street* site. You can find out what's new in *Emmerdale* at the Village Hall; get village history and photos of your favourite characters at Keepers Cottage; visit The Woolpack for the latest gossip and competitions and check out the shop for Emmerdale merchandise. You can even send a postcard. The site is a little slow due to the constant advertising.

Both *Emmerdale* and *Coronation Street* are hosted by www.G-Wizz.com, who also host sites for Granada, Yorkshire TV, LWT and Tyne Tees television.

www.emmerdale.clara.net
THE UNOFFICIAL EMMERDALE SITE

☺☺☺
COUNTRY UK

An eccentric site run by a true fan with a less fussy approach than the official site, it is divided up into sections in which you can see things such as future plotlines – spoilers. There are links to other *Emmerdale* fan sites, a weekly poll, a message board and you can send a postcard.

www.bbc.co.uk/eastenders
THE OFFICIAL EASTENDERS PAGE

☺☺☺☺
COUNTRY UK

A page from the massive BBC site which is split into several sections. You can catch up on the latest stories, get hints on future storylines, play games and competitions, get pictures of the stars and vote in their latest poll. You can also reminisce in the 'Remember When' section if you're old enough and take a virtual tour and view Albert Square with the Walford Cam.

www.familyaffairs.co.uk
FAMILY AFFAIRS UNOFFICIAL

☺☺☺
COUNTRY UK

A massive site dedicated to the goings on in Charnham, you can download whole episodes if you like, otherwise there's the usual collection of interviews, stories and pictures.

www.summerbay.co.uk
STREWTH, IT'S A HOME AND AWAY SITE
☺☺☺☺

COUNTRY
AUSTRALIA

As you'd expect, a bright and breezy site, in which you can learn all the facts about the characters that inhabit Summer Bay. There's also loads in the way of things to do.

www.hollyoaks.com
THE OFFICIAL HOLLYOAKS WEB SITE
☺☺☺☺☺

COUNTRY UK

A really cool site with lots on it, you can subscribe to the fortnightly newsletter, peek behind the scenes, catch up on the latest news and chat with fellow fans. There's also all the usual photos and downloads to be had.

www.baxendale.u-net.com/ramsayst/
NEIGHBOURS WORLDWIDE FANPAGES
☺☺☺☺

COUNTRY UK

You can also find them at www.ramsay-street.co.uk. This is a labour of love by the fans of *Neighbours*, it has everything you need: storylines past, present and future, info on all the characters, clips from some episodes, complete discographies of the singing stars and access to all the related web sites through the links page. Unfortunately you can't buy *Neighbours* merchandise from the site.

www.soapweb.co.uk
THE LATEST SOAP NEWS
☺☺☺☺ Can't be bothered with visiting each site sepa-
COUNTRY UK rately? Then try Soap Web. Here you can keep
up-to-date on all the soaps, even the Australian
and American ones.

www.unmissabletv.com
WHAT'S ON THAT'S UNMISSABLE
☺☺☺☺ A site that's dedicated to all that's best on UK
COUNTRY UK TV, with links and features on all the
programmes including soaps, there are also
special features on all the 'in' programmes.

Web cameras

One of the most fascinating features on the internet is the ability to tap into some CCTV or specially set up web cameras from all around the world.

www.I-spy.com
THE MOTHER OF ALL WEB CAM DIRECTORIES

☺ ☺ ☺
COUNTRY USA

A directory of over 3,000 sites and a great starting point to the world of web cam. Easy-to-use, but as with all these sites you need patience.

For hundreds more web cameras try these sites:
www.allcam.com
www.webviews.co.uk
www.webcamworld.com.

Stop press

The world wide web continually moves on and we've added this section to catch sites that we missed in the first draft. All are good and will be fully reviewed in the next edition.

Advice

www.canteen.ie Although still under construction this Irish site offers very good advice and support for teenagers on cancer in its many forms.

www.coolnurse.com A slowish, but good looking American site whose cool nurse dishes out medical advice on all those problems you'd rather suss out privately.

www.iwannaknow.org All you need to know about sexual health from the American Social Health Association.

www.kidshealth.org An American site full of good health advice from a highly respected organisation, the Nemours Foundation.

www.patters.demon.co.uk/ An excellent site with advice on how to deal with diabetes.

Magazines

www.teentoday.co.uk Lots to do here, with everything from articles, competitions to an excellent chat section – lots of adverts too.

www.teenfront.com Slow but worth it when you're in as there are good sections on music, style, games as well as sport. It's even got it's own radio station.

www.thej.net The Junction says it's Europe's most popular teen and student, chat and discussion site – who are we to argue. Great design.

Magic

www.magictricks.co.uk The UK's leading magic tricks store, with plenty to choose from and some to learn.

www.cardtricks.org.uk Over 70 card tricks to learn and show off.

Music

www.ukclubculture.co.uk A really good-looking site, which has you need to know about clubbing, plus trips on fashion and competitions.

www.cluboxed.co.uk Sample the latest releases and future club classics as well chat to fellow clubbers at the Global Underground.

Phones

www.studentmobiles.com Special deals on phones, competitions and you can download over 100 ring tones – at £2.99 a go.

Shopping – fashion

www.noflysonus.com A street fashion retailer with a really cool-looking site.

Sport

www.**activitiesonline.co.uk** This site has loads of
activities, sports, clubs and information on how
to get involved – excellent.
www.**theaward.org** The official site of the Duke
of Edinburgh award scheme.

Students

www.**infoyouth.com** It's got a university guide,
careers help and information on what you could
get up to in a gap year.

Index

This is not a comprehensive index, but should help you out when you can't think which section to look in.

animals 81–87, 133–136
arts 71
atlas 78
bands 106
biography 80
bullying 15
cards 59
careers 16, 189, 206
classics 72, 75
clubbing 206
concerts 117
cookies 34
classified ads 158
clip art 74
colleges 188
crosswords 56
dictionaries 54, 66–71, 76–77, 87
directories 35, 61, 66–71
discount cards 190
drugs 17
economics 77
education, general 60–65
encyclopaedias 66–71, 87
environment 83
fantasy 142–146
fantasy league 50
films 97–101
film companies 99
finance 17, 189

French 77
galleries 71–74
gap year 189, 206
geography 77–79
German 77
government 90
Harry Potter 145–146
health 18, 205
history 79–83
horoscopes 23
IQ tests 58
information technology 87
MP3 102
magazines 40, 93, 109–111, 124–132, 143, 152, 166, 191, 205
maps 78
maths 88
motorbikes 24
money 17, 189
museums 71–74
music
  theory 89–90
  information 115
  entertainment 117–118
Napster 103
nature 83–87
phone numbers 140
politics 90
price checkers 149

puzzles 56
quizzes 57
racism 19
radio 119–121
relationships 20
religion 91
royal family 80
science 91–94
school
  curriculum 60–66, 71
  problems 13–15
science fiction 96, 142–146
search engines
  general 34, 65, 70
sex 20
soaps 199–203
space 95–96
Spanish 77
stars 29, 107
stress 21
text messaging 138–140
thesaurus 69
ticket agents 98, 117
universities 188, 206
virus checker 39
weather 122
what's on 98, 109–111, 115–118
work 16–17
working abroad 189–190, 206